THE PRINCIPLES AND PRACTICE
OF
HYPNOANALYSIS

THE PRINCIPLES AND PRACTICE

OF

HYPNOANALYSIS

By

JEROME M. SCHNECK, A.B., M.D.

Clinical Associate Professor of Psychiatry
State University of New York
Downstate Medical Center
New York City
Founder and Past President
The Society for Clinical and Experimental Hypnosis

CHARLES C THOMAS • **PUBLISHER**

Springfield • Illinois • U.S.A.

Published and Distributed Throughout the World by
CHARLES C THOMAS • PUBLISHER
BANNERSTONE HOUSE
301-327 East Lawrence Avenue, Springfield, Illinois, U.S.A.
NATCHEZ PLANTATION HOUSE
735 North Atlantic Boulevard, Fort Lauderdale, Florida, U.S.A.

With THOMAS BOOKS careful attention is given to all details of manufacturing and design. It is the Publisher's desire to present books that are satisfactory as to their physical qualities and artistic possibilities and appropriate for their particular use. THOMAS BOOKS will be true to those laws of quality that assure a good name and good will.

Prnited in the Untied States of America
S-4

To Shirley

PREFACE

THIS BOOK is based on almost twenty years of personal experience with hypnoanalytic methods and concepts. It is an outgrowth of my clinical work, reflections, and points of view. The contributions of others are integrated into this account when they are significantly related to the basic material I have seen fit to present. Historical and theoretical issues are incorporated selectively to round out a view of hypnoanalysis and to place it in proper perspective.

The present work contains much discussion and data that have not, until now, appeared in print. Yet additional, unpublished clinical material has not been included because I have wanted to avoid redundancy, to enhance readability, and to permit the information recorded here to serve as representative illustrations of themes I wish to emphasize. Among these themes are some pertaining to procedures, insights, and concepts that I have introduced or developed. They include the two-stage hand levitation technique of hypnotic induction, the concept of depth reversal during termination of the hypnotic state, hypnosis and the concept of attitude toward suggestibility, a proposed phylogenetic conception of hypnosis, the hypnosis-death concept, the concept of dynamic hypnotic age regression, the concept of iatropsychology, the concept of assurance of illness reversibility, the concept of hypnotic scene visualization, the concept of defensive productivity in relation to hypnosis, the nature of hidden determinants in deceptive requests for hypnoanalysis, interviews with the therapist in fantasy, the concept of pseudo-malingering, and the analysis of hypnotic sensory and motor phenomena.

Various topics mentioned in the table of contents are not confined only to their respective sections. They appear also in other sections. Some topics that are difficult to define in a few words are not mentioned at all in the table of contents. Should a reader be interested in finding a particular theme, it would be advisable for him to examine both the table of contents and the index.

Descriptions of patients are brief or detailed as seems to me to be appropriate in each case. No effort is made to present extensive data about individual patients from clinical records. Involved reports of such patients are available in my journal publications, as noted in the references, and in articles by others as commented on in the text. I considered the idea of presenting one case extensively but it would serve little good purpose. Treatment of patients varies no much that one such report can easily be misleading. It would not warrant the space required. A few books that stress individual cases are on hand for those interested in that type of approach. My preference has been for the presentation, at lesser or greater length, of a rich array of case illustrations or case references to clarify the concepts that have constituted the core of my work.

Were this book written in a very conventional and traditional manner, there would be separate chapters on history, theory, induction and termination, hypnoanalytic techniques, transference and countertransference, case studies, and other specifically designated areas. Although certain sections deal predominantly with these themes, I have found that I could achieve wider and more intensive coverage, saying more easily the things I have wanted to say, by adopting a more fluid, discursive, and less structured format. I hope this will appeal to readers more than the formal textbook style.

I do not deal with general issues of psychotherapy except at times when some of them relate in a special way to points in the material dealing with hypnoanalysis specifically. Themes in the broader field of hypnotherapy are introduced only to the degree that they help to reenforce, integrate, and consolidate discussions of hypnoanalytic endeavors. Books on hypnotherapy are readily available for those concerned, including my own as noted in the references. Readers can come by writings on psychotherapy and psychoanalysis in their broader aspects by consulting current literature.

As I take into consideration what I have set out to do and the text as it now stands, it seems to me that this book on the principles and practice of hypnoanalysis is, so far as I know, the only volume with such extensive coverage that has as yet been published.

JEROME M. SCHNECK, M.D.

CONTENTS

Page

Preface vii

PART ONE

1. Definition and Nature of Hypnoanalysis 3
2. Historical Antecedents and Influences 4
3. Value of Hypnoanalysis 16
4. Length of Treatment and Frequency of Sessions 19
5. Hypnoanalysis and the Concept of Trance Depth 22
6. Denial of Hypnosis 25
7. Initiation of Hypnoanalysis 27
8. Misleading Requests for Hypnoanalysis, Hypnotic Induction,
   and Misunderstandings about Hypnosis 30
9. Hypnotizability, Reactions to Hypnosis, Transference and
   Countertransference 32
10. The Two-stage Hand Levitation Technique, and Induction
    Phenomena 36
11. The Concept of Depth Reversal during Termination of the
    Hypnotic State 39
12. Flexibility on Starting a Hypnoanalysis 42
13. Resistance and Transference 43

PART TWO

1. Hypnoanalytic Explorations 51
2. Hypnosis, Hypnoanalysis, and Psychological Test Methods . . 52
3. Hypnoanalysis, Transference, and Problems of Symptom Relief . 56
4. Hypnosis and a Concept of Attitude Toward Suggestibility . 60

ix

Page

5. Transference, Symptom Alleviation, and Hypnoanalysis . . 61
6. Spontaneous Sensory and Motor Phenomena 63
7. Theories of Hypnosis, the Nature of Hypnosis, and a Proposed
   Phylogenetic Conception of Hypnosis 69
8. Abreaction, Insight, and Related Concerns in Psychoanalytic
   Hypnotherapy 81

PART THREE

1. Hypnoanalysis and Productiveness 89
2. Exhibitionism and Deception 90
3. Hypnoanalysis and the Hypnosis-death Concept 93
4. Visual Imagery and Hallucinations in Hypnoanalysis . . . 95
5. Hypnotic Contradiction of Waking Verbalizations, and Enhanced Verbalizations 98
6. Perceptiveness and Patients' Attitudes Toward Hypnotic Experience 99
7. Regression and Revivification in Hypnoanalysis 101
8. The Concept of Dynamic Hypnotic Age Regression 103
9. Hypnotic Hallucinatory Experience 106
10. Spontaneous Nocturnal Dreams, Hypnotic Dreams, and Hypno-
    analysis 107
11. Hypnotic Imagery, and Sensory and Motor Phenomena during
    Hypnoanalysis 109
12. Applicability and Efficacy of Hypnotic Techniques 112
13. Diagnostic Categories and Amenability to Hypnoanalysis . . 113
14. Anxiety and Hypnoanalysis 114
15. The Concept of Assurance of Illness Reversibility 116
16. Limitations on Symptom Relief, and Anxiety-depression Cor-
    relations 117

PART FOUR

1. Varying Views of the Structure of a Hypnoanalysis 123
2. Elaboration of Psychoanalytic Observations 126

3. Hypnosis-rebirth and Hypnosis-death Themes with Anthropological Observations 127
4. Hypnosis, Transference, and Transference Analysis 129
5. Spontaneous Hypnotic and Self-hypnotic States 131
6. Self-hypnotic Dreams in Hypnoanalysis 133
7. The Concept of Hypnotic Scene Visualization 136
8. Hypnoanalysis and Hypnotic Hallucinations 137
9. The Concept of Defensive Productivity in Relation to Hypnosis . 138
10. Multiple Personalities 140
11. Behavior, Expectation, and Artifact 141

PART FIVE

1. Confirmation of Psychoanalytic Observations 145
2. The Nature of Hidden Determinants in Deceptive Requests for Hypnoanalysis 147
3. Hypnotic Imagery and Second Selves 150
4. Appearance and Behavior in Hypnoanalysis 153
5. Successes and Failures and Attitudes Toward Treatment . . 157
6. Motivation and Goal, Intellectual and Emotional Insight . . 161
7. Variations in Spontaneous Verbalizations 163
8. Dreams and Hypnoanalysis 164
9. Doctor-patient Relationships and Behavior 165
10. Spontaneous Remissions 167
11. Hypnoanalysis and Psychoanalytic Explorations 168
12. Automatic, Compulsive, and Impulsive Drawing 171
13. Reactions to Hypnotic Behavior and Settings as Reflections of Personality Attributes 173
14. Anxiety, Hypnoanalysis, and Somatic Symptomatology . . . 175
15. Dependency, Action, and Magic in Hypnotherapy and Psychoanalysis 176
16. Concentrated Hypnoanalytic Measures and Transference Implications 177

Page

17. Interviews with the Therapist in Fantasy, Transference and Countertransference 181
18. Spontaneous Regressions, Hypnoanalysis, and the Superego . 186
19. Notions of Superficial and Deep Psychotherapy 190
20. Hypnotic Dreams and Scene Visualizations 191
21. Aspects of Denial, Hypnotic Paralysis, and Sleep Paralysis . . 193
22. Denial of Hypnosis, Alleged Simulation of Hypnosis, and the Concept of Pseudo-malingering 194
23. Hypnoanalysis and Phobic Symptomatology 195
24. The Past and the Present 196
25. Hypnosis-homosexuality Equations 197
26. Rapid Investigations, Premature Termination of Treatment, and Hypnotic Control 198
27. Dynamics of Interest in Hypnosis 200
28. Hypnoanalysis and Psychoanalysis 202

Name Index 211
Subject Index 215

THE PRINCIPLES AND PRACTICE
OF
HYPNOANALYSIS

1. Definition and Nature of Hypnoanalysis

Hypnoanalysis is best defined, I believe, as an area of psychotherapy that combines the principles and practice of psychoanalysis with the principles and practice of hypnotherapy. It possesses complex facets, variations, and applications. Methods and thought in hypnoanalytic practice have origins that center around two primary time periods. One is the second half of the eighteenth century with the observations and practice of Mesmer whose work is often equated with the beginnings of scientific psychotherapy. The other is the late nineteenth century with the contributions of Freud constituting the core of psychoanalytic psychotherapy, an important ingredient of what we have come to call dynamic psychiatry. Misunderstandings about hypnoanalysis are based partly on the belief that its techniques and concepts are rooted essentially in pre-Freudian developments and in the early work of Freud when he was still actively concerned with the practice of hypnotherapy. Yet it should be obvious that the assumption is unwarranted and untenable. The definition I have offered of hypnoanalysis underscores the role of psychoanalytic principles and implies that the fundamental body of Freud's psychoanalytic contributions is involved in the essence of hypnoanalysis. The major elements in these contributions followed his relinquishing interest in his own therapeutic use of hypnosis.

In more recent years there have been developments in psychoanalysis based on studies regarded by many analysts as an outgrowth of traditional Freudian strivings and aims while still confined to its basic bonds. Also, there have been contributions labelled neo-Freudian and post-Freudian. The essence of such explorations or advances can be incorporated into the growing area of hypnoanalysis. Its flexibility in this respect may indeed be a distinct advantage. Whether problems in adaptability on this score will arise in the future cannot be foretold now. As I have pointed out on other occasions, one of the advantages of hypno-therapy in general is the fact that hypnotic methods often permit integration with theoretic concepts of several schools of thought that place stress on different aspects of therapeutuc processes and goals.

2. Historical Antecedents and Influences

There is little of specific significance in the historical develop-ment of hypnoanalysis prior to the work of the eighteenth and early nineteenth century physician Franz Anton Mesmer (22). "Crises" and trance experiences of one form or other were known long before his time, however, and some data pertaining to primi-tive peoples are of interest in connection with our subject. Probably the paleomedicine of ancient man involved, in certain instances, trance activity such as is found even today among primitive tribes. Concepts of disease among them include the influence of spirits and the power of offended gods. Some of the ingredients in these forces are perhaps not a far step from the superego operations that we describe now within a context of normal psychology and psycho-pathology and that we choose to regard as more sophisticated. The healing trance among primitives is incorporated into magico-religious medicine with its supernaturalism, yet there is present at the same time a holistic view of man and disease supplying a unitary element that is in many circles a concern of medicine today (23).

Frazer described trance states among primitive peoples and he observed that some of these states were death-like (24). Among certain groups such states were hardly distinguished from death. In the course of investigations of hypnoanalysis, I discovered more recently in clinical experience that some patients unconsciously equate hypnosis and death, so I was taken by the later discovery in my readings of Frazer's observations among primitives (Schneck, 25). He was not alone in these encounters and other reports on such trance rites and identifications have been published more recently (26). To the degree that trance may be equated with death, it can be equated too with rebirth. This identification also is not confined to primitives. I encounter it in clinical hypno-analytic settings (Schneck, 27). There are many accounts of trance experience among primitives and it is unnecessary to describe them in detail. I think one example of the role it plays in the medicine, magic, and religion of such groups, is that given by Sigerist and this is sufficient for our purposes (28). He tells of the medicine man among the Loango of French Equatorial Africa. The medicine man may enter a trance at night at which time his soul leaves him to consult ancestral spirits. On its return, the diviner is told about the cause of the patient's illness. Trance and primitive groups will be mentioned again later in this book.

Several writers have told of the use of hypnosis among the ancients, and thereafter in some settings not long before the work of Mesmer. The accounts are difficult to evaluate precisely but the material on hand about the healing efforts involving the use of hypnosis is similar to, or suggestive of some measures that have continued to be employed into modern times. It is not hard to come by cursory references to trance experience in ancient China, India, Egypt and Greece (29-31). Magnets were used frequently in conjunction with hypnotic procedures, and references to magnetic healing effects may be found in connection with the activities of Cardan and Paracelsus, before Mesmer.

Mesmer was and still is a controversial figure (33). Accounts about him are readily available and his personality need not concern us here (Schneck, 32). His ideas about animal magnetism may be discerned from his famous *Mémoire* with its twenty-seven propositions (34). George Rosen, in his contribution to one of my previous books, has shown that the issues and theoretical points involved in Mesmer's views were common to the eighteenth century medical world (Schneck, 18). A study of Mesmer's methods shows that they contained ingredients of the concepts of suggestion that came to the fore later, and developed eventually into the more complex formulations taken into account now. The issue of rapport, in the doctor-patient animal magnetism contact, appears to point in the direction of the notion of transference in psychoanalytic terminology. These themes cannot be dismissed if one is to evaluate seriously the role of Mesmer in the beginnings of modern psychotherapy. In addition, it is important to note his stress on the area of "nervous disorders" and their amenability to healing. Beyond the influence of Mesmer's work on the develop-

ment of psychotherapy, it had relationships with the area of electrotherapy specifically. I have discussed this elsewhere but shall
not develop details now because they are beyond our present purpose (Schneck, 35). In any case it is worth noting that at least one
medical historian has seen Mesmer as a typical rationalist and
speculative systematist of the eighteenth century (23).

Present day interest in hypnosis has led to reevaluations, some
of which involve groups of individuals offering opinions about the
subject. At times a group would operate under the official aegis
of a prominent organization. In recent years, for example, generally favorable reports were rendered by the British Medical
Association in 1955 and the American Medical Association in
1958. Hypnoanalysis has not been singled out specifically for such
evaluations, but an important point involved in the assessment of
hypnosis in its broader aspects can apply also to hypnoanalysis in
its more limited aspects. This has to do with the investigating
committees and commissions through the years, and there have
been many in this particular area. When studying the approach
of these groups, it became clear that few individuals involved in
them had practical experience in the areas on which they passed
judgment. It seemed to me that an important feature concerning
all of the commissions is that they possess historical importance
because they have influenced the general attitudes assumed toward
the subject investigated. This applied less to the influence of these
bodies regarding specific conclusions reached in the reports. The
committees seemed inclined usually to accept unfavorable decisions and to reject favorable findings by those investigating the
subject, and this fact is pertinent to what I have referred to elsewhere as the history of scientific attitudes (Schneck, 36).

John Elliotson and James Esdaile are two proponents of mid-
nineteenth century mesmerism who may be focused on briefly for
our purposes, though they are involved primarily in the historical
aspects of medical and surgical hypnosis. Elliotson has a place
here because his activities helped to center additional attention on
the neuroses and the amenability of neurotic patients to some
relief through the mesmeric process (Schneck, 32, 37). This was
a step that continued the line of activity Mesmer himself had
embarked on, and it has its place in the history of psychotherapy.

James Esdaile accomplished his well known surgical work in India, for which he employed mesmerism in many cases, but the nature of his curiosity touches on current concerns in hypnoanalysis by virtue of some attention to mesmeric dreams. This was an area of interest that he regretted he could not pursue further (38, Schneck, 39). Esdaile was interested in dreams that involved planning, problem solving, sudden insight, and creative experience. In his well known book, *Mesmerism In India*, he wrote, "I see no reason to doubt that the mental organs can be isolated and exalted by the mesmeric influence under the direction of a skillful leader and suggester, and can readily believe that the mind, by this artificial stimulus, may be excited into more vigorous activity than when acted upon by the usual conditions of life... My psychological experiments have been very limited, partly because I fear to bewilder myself at the outset, and also from want of proper subjects to try them on [he worked with the natives of India]. The mental range of my patients is so circumscribed, that the topics of food, drink and clothing almost exhaust it, and with most of them I have no common language. But I have done enough to show me how the higher grades of somnambulism may be reached; and with more highly organized and intellectual natures, I should have good hopes of doing so." Esdaile was unable to capitalize on his observations through lack of clinical experience in psychological areas or a systematized knowledge of psychological concepts, but his comments earn him at least a small place in the history of the growth of scientific hypnosis in psychological areas.

As in the case of psychoanalysis, hypnotic practice and investigations made inroads into the content of literary productions of well known writers. Included among them are Edgar Allan Poe, Henry James, George du Maurier, Robert Browning, and Edward Bellamy (Schneck, 40-45). Du Maurier's book can be dismissed all too readily if one chooses to regard it as a sensational popularization of the hypnosis theme. I was able to show, after careful study of it, the presence of many issues of interest to students of behavioral science and to hypnoanalysts specifically. Some themes have to do with the induction of hypnosis, the hypnotized person as a sexual object, masochism of a hypnotist, the psychology of the amateur hypnotist, suggestibility, and the hypnosis-death concept (Schneck, 41). Points of general psychological interest and psychoanalytic concern have long been known to reside in myths and fables. Fairy tales have been studied in this connection. One can examine them too for items relating to hypnosis and associated phenomena. I offered one example in the form of time obliteration, a subject of interest in relation to analytic settings and more pointedly to certain aspects of hypnotic functioning and attempts at time control (Schneck, 44, 45).

The imposing figure of late nineteenth century hypnosis was, of course, the neurologist Charcot. His work and that of his colleagues was essentially experimental. It is possible to consider at length and in detail the nature of his findings, including his errors, but the point to be stressed is his well known contact with Freud, thus highlighting an important period of Freud's early psychological work, involvement with hypnosis, and the eventual departure into non-hypnotic, psychoanalytic explorations. Charcot and his assistants worked essentially with a few, select, grossly hysterical patients. His name is indelibly associated with the history of hypnosis and his authority and popularity stirred up considerable interest in it. Some have said he made hypnosis respectable (47, Schneck, 46).

A basic difference between the interests of Freud and Charcot, in the pre-analytic phase of hypnosis, is the therapeutic orientation. Freud was concerned with assisting his patients. Charcot functioned mainly experimentally and through teaching demonstrations (Schneck, 48). Thus, so far as therapeutic interest is concerned, Freud came closer to the work of Bernheim and Liébeault of the Nancy School, the group opposing the views of the Charcot or Paris School (49). For them, hypnotizability was an expression of normal behavior, whereas for Charcot hypnosis was essentially an experimental neurosis. Liébeault and Bernheim appreciated the broad range of hypnotizability in the general population along with the less dramatic manifestations of hypnotic reaction and behavior. They saw the broad therapeutic possibilities in clinical experience. Although priorities are often misleading, it has been said of Bernheim that his efforts to gain insight into human behavior, through study of suggestibility, were the first known attempts to reach a psychopathological basis for grasping the essence of behavioral motivations. A visit to him was described by William Alanson White, well known in the history of psychoanalytic developments. White said of Bernheim that he was "perhaps the best known psychotherapist in Europe at that time" (76, Schneck, 75).

Charcot's life and work were examined recently by his distinguished biographer, Georges Guillain, but the hypnotic explorations were not, in my opinion, interpreted properly, and they were deficient in facts (50). The claim was made, for example, that Charcot never checked the experiments of his co-workers and that this accounted for his errors. It was said also that he never personally hypnotized a single patient. I pointed elsewhere to the evidence refuting these views and was able to call on the classic work of Binet and Féré in support of the points I made (51, Schneck, 48). The reflections on Charcot's experience at hypnotizing have also been cast on Freud although without such sweeping accusations. I suspect Freud had more experience than his detractors would allow, and less than his uninformed supporters would like to believe (52, 53). Whereas Freud had contact with Charcot and Bernheim, I do not know that he was influenced in this area by the neurologist and neuroanatomist, Luys, whom I had occasion to discuss when presenting the presence at that time of the lesser known School of the Hospital de la Charité of which he was the main figure. This may be mentioned now parenthetically as a group combining the views of the Paris and Nancy factions (Schneck, 54). It leaned more toward the Salpêtrière faction of Charcot in its experimental and physicalist orientation, while it incorporated also the suggestion and therapeutic views of Liébeault and Bernheim (31). It seems to have retained post-Mesmeric fluidist concepts too.

Basic to the suggestion measures of the Charité group and the Nancy doctors, as well as among the hypnotherapists in the decades to follow, were the roots established by investigators before them, especially the best known of all, James Braid. His presence as an important figure on the hypnosis scene must be mentioned in connection with its historical origins, with particular relation to the suggestion theme in its experimental position and its therapeutic role. The threads of suggestion in all psychotherapy including psychoanalysis lead back to him. It is not necessary to enter into details of his conflict with Elliotson except to state that present day concepts of hypnosis and the term "hypnotism" with several derivatives stem from Braid who rejected the fluidist doctrines of animal magnetism that Elliotson retained (55).

Freud spent time in Paris with Charcot in 1885 and observed the work of Bernheim and Liébeault in 1889. He was disappointed in therapeutic results with electrotherapy. Bernheim's activities made an impression on him and he sensed the possible existence of strong forces at work within patients although these forces might be hidden from consciousness.

The origins of psychoanalysis, however, are generally credited not to these associations with Charcot and the Nancy physicians, but more properly to Freud's association with Josef Breuer who, during this period, was interested in hypnosis while conducting his general practice of medicine in Vienna. The special focus of his interest was the cathartic method consisting of spontaneous verbalizations of a patient and the discharge of emotions during the hypnotic state. His work in this field is now well known although, apparently, he was not alone in this area. The efforts of Bourru and Burot have received some attention recently (56).

Breuer collaborated with Freud, but he deferred to him as instrumental in the beginnings of psychoanalysis itself (53). Oberndorf called attention to his specific statement (57). Breuer wrote in his autobiography, "In 1880, I had observed a patient suffering from a severe hysteria, who in the course of her illness displayed such peculiar symptoms as to convince me that here a glimpse was being offered into deeper layers of psychopathological processes. The insights then gained were presented by S. Freud and myself, first in a short preliminary study and later in the *Studies On Hysteria* by Breuer and Freud. This book, which was rather unfavorably received at first, went into its fourth edition last year. It is the seed from which psychoanalysis was developed by Freud."

As is well known and so frequently emphasized, Freud eventually relinquished his work with hypnosis. He seemed to believe he found this essential on clinical grounds. Stress was placed, for example, on difficulties in adequate hypnotizability of many patients for the purpose of obtaining meaningful and sustained results. The issue of hypnotizability and the need to relinquish hypnosis for achieving lasting changes are no longer tenable in the light of investigations that have taken place more recently. These consist of more extensive clinical observations and activities, and reevaluations with deeper understandings of personality functioning as well as the development of therapeutic measures to cope with such functioning. It is particularly important to note that to a great extent these strides stem from new knowledge obtained through psychoanalytic insights introduced by Freud.

Even for his time, however, the reasons given by Freud for relinquishing hypnosis appear to be questionable on clinical grounds alone. It would have been possible to develop therapeutuc techniques further while working within the setting of hypnotic states achieved by patients in his practice. Furthermore, the issue of depth of hypnosis in a classical sense has been demonstrated repeatedly as unnecessary for good therapeutic results and this would have applied also in Freud's contact with his patients. When reading his work on *Studies On Hysteria* one finds indications of clinical activity moving in the direction of what has since been developed by others. One may infer that had Freud continued this way the likelihood is that he might have developed essentially along lines now familiar to us and still associated with the area of hypnosis investigation.

Certain elements in his rejection of hypnosis have been examined by others (58). In an evaluation of this theme several years ago, I studied in detail the issue of counter-transference in the step he took (Schneck, 59). Stress was placed on the incident that Freud mentioned in his autobiography. He was treating hypnotically a woman in whom he was tracing the origins of attacks of pain. She emerged from the hypnosis and threw her arms around him. The unexpected entrance of a servant relieved them, he said, of a painful discussion. There was now a tacit understanding that hypnosis would be discontinued. He denied the relation of her behavior to his personal attraction. He felt he now understood the "mysterious element" behind hypnosis. "In order to exclude it, or at all events to isolate it, it was necessary to abandon hypnosis."

Of course, this is questionable. In the course of developing psychoanalysis, many similar and related events have taken place, but they have not led to the abandonment of psychoanalytic measures. One might rightly say that for his time the step was more understandable. This may be so, but with the accumulation of additional knowledge it is note-worthy that he did not return to hypnosis. More important, his immediate followers did not return to it in a meaningful and fruitful way. Having gone on to other interests there is no reason for one to expect him necessarily to have taken it up again. But it would have been desirable in the years that followed for a correction to have been made in the original claims for needs to abandon it. The incident mentioned above is especially interesting in the light of allegations made afterwards regarding the countertransference theme in Breuer's reluctance to continue with investigations that pointed in the direction of the development of psychoanalysis. The transference reaction, the "mysterious element" that led allegedly to the abandonment of hypnosis in the aforementioned patient of Freud, did not result later in the exclusion of psychoanalytic methods as they did the hypnotic measures in this case. Understanding such reactions and capitalizing on them were as pertinent at the time of that therapeutic encounter as they were to become later.

Freud's statement, after commenting on this event, that hypnosis had been of great help in the cathartic method and that "it seemed no easy task to find a substitute for it" contradicts the frequently encountered implication that better methods were being developed by him to substitute for the hypnotic techniques. He admitted his perplexity until he recalled Bernheim's work with posthypnotic amnesia and steps taken to break through the amnesia.

Difficulties in hypnotizing, which has also been stressed in connection with the rejection of hypnosis, is questionable too in connection with its abandonment because of the obvious point that the classical psychoanalytic procedures turned out to be applicable to a relatively small proportion of psychiatric patients, and for various reasons. Furthermore, when the shift was made by Freud from hypnotic inductions to attempts to further a patient's associations by applying a hand to the patient's forehead, Freud observed, "No doubt this seemed a more laborious process than putting them into hypnosis, but it might prove highly instructive." Eventually Freud took up points about analysis of resistance and transference, but as is or should be well known now, neither of these concerns have anything to do realistically with the necessity to reject hypnosis. Such analytic efforts can take place within the hypnotic setting.

There is much more that can be said about the issues mentioned above, but the reader is directed to the original publication containing such discussion (Schneck, 59). Various relevant references are given which perpetuate the questionable points of view regarding Freud's decision. These include assertions by Brill (60) and by Jones (61).

Statements have been made by others regarding this issue of Freud and hypnosis. For example, it has been said of him that his hesitancy to employ hypnosis for therapeutic purposes may have reflected a reaction formation related to his own fantasies of omnipotence (62). Need it be said, however, that regardless of claims, accurate or inaccurate, and additional understandings of Freud as a person, his major work stands on its own merit in historical perspective. And as for the role of his own personality in all of this, I might add one additional point which may come closer to the core of his rejection of hypnosis. The reading of his life as detailed by himself and others shows indications of his considerable ambition and drive for prestige. There was great striving for originality and the desire to make a name for himself. Hypnosis had a long tradition behind it. Its history highlighted many names already deeply engraved in the pattern of its development. And in his own time, men like Bernheim and Charcot had achieved great stature. I am inclined toward the view that Freud, in his own drive for recognition, may have been reluctant to take his place as one of many. He seemed more to wish to stand alone. In this wish, the abandonment of a tradition bound subject, with a line of outstanding leaders identified with it, may have been essential for him. In taking his stand, whether he did so consciously or not, and I suspect it was the former, he did reach his goal. He does stand alone at the pinnacle of this scientific development.

The impact of Freud and his work is reflected in the development during the twentieth century of what I have designated as "iatropsychology" (Schneck, 74). In seventeenth century medicine there was a trend characterized by stress on chemical ideas, and iatrochemistry and iatrochemists came into being. Counterparts of iatrochemists were the iatrophysicists, also called iatromechanists or iatromathematicians. Franz de le Boe, also known as Sylvius, represented the iatrochemists, and Giorgio Baglivi and Giovanni Borelli were representatives of the iatrophysicists. Iatropsychology is reflected especially in the area of psychiatry, but its impact is felt in other areas of medical practice. Its influence shows in the current focus of attention on "psychosomatics." Although psychobiology played a role in its emergence, the predominant weight of Freud and the psychoanalytic school is fundamental to iatropsychology today. The iatropsychologist deals mainly with psychological concepts in medical practice although his medical training and knowledge reenfore his judgments and govern his activities. But his interests lie basically in psychological techniques. Needless to say, there are extremists in this group as in any other.

Emotional allegiances to Freud and his work followed the development of psychoanalysis. Intense identifications with him obscured potential scientific horizons, blocking legitimate evaluations of theory and technique. If inroads can be made into the destructive blocks stemming from emotional ties to tradition, potential energy may be released in many workers capable of making further explorations into the realm of hypnotic research and therapy. The powerful influence of outworn allegiances and identifications can serve only as an undesirable deterrant.

In order to appreciate fully the wealth of hypnotic experience accumulated over the years and capable of being put to use within the framework of hypnoanalytic activity, one should turn to some of the writings of investigators who published findings during the years Freud was occupied with his original hypnosis interests and developing psychoanalytic concerns. Only a few of these investigators need be mentioned. Their books are well known and comprise part of a lasting, meaningful collection of hypnosis literature. The men include Moll (63), Forel (64), Bramwell (65), Janet (66), Prince (67), and Sidis (68).

Janet is usually given special attention in some of the controversies regarding the origin of psychoanalysis. The man and his work basically have strong supporters. But significant influences of his work on the ideas advanced by Freud are generally denied. Janet was, however, an excellent psychopathologist and much interested in problems of hysteria. It is believed, however, that he could not discard the notion of hysteria as a degenerative disease. He influenced the work of Morton Prince (69) who was concerned, as was Freud, with mental processes operating beyond conscious awareness. The point of co-conscious functioning is associated with Prince. Also, he was closely identified with the issue of multiple personalities. Within recent years there has been an increase in writings on this theme, and some of them have been by investigators in the field of hypnoanalysis. The questions regarding them have arisen again through the behavioral features evident in some patients studied in hypnotherapy conducted within the framework of psychoanalytic theory and interpretation. It is usually agreed that Prince did not accept the view of an unconscious in the Freudian sense. Also, the opinion has been expressed that Prince was influenced by ideas such as those favored by von Hartmann (Schneck, 32).

During the third and fourth decades of this century some investigators contributed quite meaningfully to the growing body of information about hypnosis. Not all of it has been of significance in the growth of hypnoanalysis specifically. An example is the work of Hull and his collaborators who placed stress on academic laboratory and experimental settings (70). On the other hand, Paul Schilder made worthy efforts to integrate hypnotic methods with the new knowledge of psychoanalysis and he enters into the historical perspectives of this subject (71).

The use of the term, hypno-analysis, stems from work during the first World War when combinations of abreactive methods and reeducational efforts were employed (72). Afterwards, the same term was used for a variety of therapeutic approaches some of which were uncovering methods, but others of which had no special relation to analysis in terms of psychoanalyatic theory and technique. Hadfield's work during World War I, designated hypnoanalysis, consisted of cathartic hypnosis combined with reeducational measures. Simmel also used hypnosis during that war and he described his methods as having involved hypno-analysis. "A combination of analytic-cathartic hypnosis with analytical conversations during the waking state and in deep hypnosis, has given me a method which on an average of two or three sittings brought about relief of the symptoms" (77). Elsewhere we find, "One of my patients suffered from a shaking tremor of his right arm, with peculiar circular movements of the thumb and forefinger, which looked like a one-sided Parkinson. Hypno-analysis revealed that during a furious hand-grenade fight, he was just on the point of setting a grenade fuse with a screw-like movement, when suddenly he was blown over. He lost consciousness with his rage undischarged" (78).

Hypnoanalysis as a descriptive term is used loosely at times even now, but this volume focusses on those contributions most meaningful to the framework of psychoanalysis itself. The emphasis on hypnoanalysis in more recent years, while given by some investigators operating essentially independently, has been reenforced by the interest shown in the field of hypnosis in general. This interest was markedly emphasized following the second World War with the founding by the present writer of The Society for Clinical and Experimental Hypnosis (Schneck, 96). Many of the contributions to the subject of hypnoanalysis may be seen in the pages of its publications.

3. Value of Hypnoanalysis

It is reasonable to ask whether hypnoanalysis can, in a broad sense, offer any promise for therapy that other methods of psychotherapy cannot. An answer may be prefaced by the claim that it is legitimate to explore the possibilities of hypnoanalysis as a field of scientific and medical concern were it not even possible to make any special therapeutic claims for it at this time. However, clinical experience has revealed already some rewarding returns. It is my feeling, and in this I know I have the support of others, that no form of psychotherapy can reliably claim for itself a position of pre-eminence in its ability to assist psychiatric patients, regardless of occasional assertions by adamant adherents to special techniques or theoretical formulations. Rogers has reiterated that we are in a period when so many divergent explanations are given for a single event (73). I think the claims of some adherents, to a particular point of view regarding therapeutic efficacy, may appear to be true if the element of selectivity in accepting only special patients is disregarded as an influence on such impressions. Also, as is well known, opinions differ on what should be considered good evidence of therapeutic change. These issues are of general psychiatric concern and need not give rise at this point to extensive discussion. They will, however, be kept in mind constantly as various aspects of hypnoanalysis are described. For further exploration of the general theme, and some insight into diverse methods of therapeutic investigation, reference may be made to books such as those edited by Burton (1), Wolff (2), and Wortis (3).

Despite benefits that can be derived therapeutically in work with hypnoanalysis, I do not think of it in terms of a substitute for traditional psychoanalysis, psychoanalytically oriented therapies, or other types of therapeutic measures. It is more meaningful to regard it as an additional method that may be of benefit for many patients. Some patients may be helped by hypnoanalysis as an initial therapeutic relationship. A number may find it rewarding following disappointments with previous attempts at treatment. Others may discover that it contributes further to therapeutic gains already established. One may say that for some patients who find they are capable of working effectively with a few of the technical aids among many within the framework of hypnoanalysis, this psychoanalytic variant supplies worthwhile returns. One will encounter among such patients those who may be able to work well with therapies that do not involve the use of hypnosis. Others may find the hypnotic setting especially helpful. This is consistent with our awareness that patients vary in their ability to progress therapeutically in settings involving differing theoretical orientations. Should it ever be discovered that it is possible to foresee which patients are likely to benefit most in therapeutic settings involving different theoretical orientations and therapeutic methods, a larger number of people will be assisted with their problems than is the case now, and fewer changes in therapies and therapists will be likely to occur among them. Of course the personalities not only of patients but of therapists too would have to be taken into consideration as well as other complicated and often poorly understood factors that influence therapy. These remarks should not be taken, therefore, as broad, simple generalizations that ignore complex ingredients in this admittedly intricate problem.

Although it is not an essential issue of practical concern, one may ask as part of an over-all view of hypnoanalysis whether it is still psychoanalysis. The question serves as a reminder of remarks by Horney when she introduced her book on "the neurotic personality of our time" (4). Her question was based on certain deviations in interpretations from those of Freud. Her comment stressed that the answer would depend on what one regarded as essential in psychoanalysis. In her case this meant that if the essential constituted the sum of Freud's theories, her therapy was not psychoanalysis. If the essential consisted of basic views on the role and expression of unconscious processes and their being brought to a level of awareness, the therapy was psychoanalysis. The implication was, of course, that psychoanalysis must grow. In the case of hypnoanalysis, techniques would be stressed rather than theory, if a parallel were to be drawn with Horney's claim. The reason is that, at present, practitioners of hypnoanalysis are probably influenced more by Freud's basic ideas and subsequent developments in "orthodox" analysis than by deviations categorized as neo-Freudian. This does not imply, however, that newer views under the latter heading have not become integrated into the thinking and practices of hypnoanalysts. Certain developments in hypnoanalysis appear to parallel the thinking of investigators who may be regarded as post-Freudian. Some of the observations stemming from the experiences of Horney and Sullivan would be difficult to ignore, and at the same time we recognize that it is frequently hard to decide whether or not allegedly new views were or were not in fact inherent in Freud's original formulations (5, 6). As the reader encounters the discussions that appear in this volume, he may note relationships to concurrent writings of Alexander, Rado, and others (97-100). He might also bear in mind what I had occasion to say in a discussion at the first annual conference of the American Academy of Psychotherapists in 1956. Were there to be "...a terminology in common introduced, a large number of the happenings in actual practice among therapists of very many so-called 'schools' would be remarkably alike" (Schneck, 101).

Were one to inquire whether a general statement can be offered to account for the desirability of adding hypnoanalysis to other therapies in use currently, I should say that the most meaningful response would be that some patients work effectively in the hypnotic setting with hypnotic methods, and in fact appear to do better with them than they seem to do when the hypnotic setting is excluded (Schneck, 21). We shall be discussing in detail the various ingredients that constitute the building blocks for this generalization. This claim of mine is offered now in contrast to the most frequent argument in favor of its use, namely the emphasis on time and short-term treatment.

4. Length of Treatment and Frequency of Sessions

Although the appeal regarding the time factor has a measure of merit, the widespread exaggerations made for it do not. As for the issue of time, it would be fair to state as an appropriate evaluation that, properly conducted, a hypnoanalysis for any one patient should consume no more time than would an analysis without the inclusion of an hypnotic setting. It may be claimed further that, all else being equal (the nature of the neurotic conflicts, for example), the addition of an hypnotic relationship to the conventional interchange offers the possibility, if not the probability, that the analysis would take less time, often considerably less time if the patient demonstrates his ability to function well with hypnotic methods.

What are some of the assertions? "Orthodox" psychoanalysis may take two years or more. Such analysis and neo-Freudian equivalents may consume even five years or more. Hypnoanalysis, it is boasted, may take only a few weeks, or at most a few months. At times the number of hours is mentioned specifically. Forty hours to one hundred hours is one example. I suspect this type of assertion is made for hypnoanalysis conducted in special settings with patients who may have little opportunity to continue longer on the basis of their own expressed needs. My personal experience has been that some patients with relatively circumscribed problems have been helped in less than forty hours of treatment, whereas those with more far-reaching difficulties have required more than one hundred hours. Severe characterological difficulties, assuming they can be worked through, have required several hundred hours of intensive treatment for significant modification. The span of time required for these efforts will depend also on frequency of visits. This may vary from daily interviews to interviews spaced at weekly or semi-weekly intervals. In private practice, two or three interviews weekly to start are often sufficient for many patients, but visits once a week are common and are often utilized effectively. The latter arrangement may appear to be unusual when compared with what had long been the "rule" in conventional arrangements, but I suppose decisions on this score must be based too on whether one wishes to consider or to ignore the economic capacities and status of many patients while allowing for payment of fees within the usual range encountered in psychiatric practice.

The issue of length of treatment and the influence of hypnosis on it brings up the question of frequency with which hypnotic interviews are introduced in relation to the sum of all sessions. The only reasonable answer is that hypnosis need be incorporated into treatment whenever the issues that are being dealt with would seem to warrant it, and as long as the patient continues to work with hypnotic methods effectively at such times. Under certain circumstances there would appear to be no need to use a hypnotic setting. For example, a patient need not employ it when describing routine affairs which, at that point at least, could be revealed essentially on this unmodified conversational level. Another instance is when a patient is supplying historical data from an essentially preliminary, factual point of view. An additional example consists of interviews taken up with discussions of the content and significance of hypnotic sessions themselves. The ratio of hypnotic to non-hypnotic interviews varies considerably among patients. The hypnotic settings may represent, for some, only a small portion of total treatment time. For others, the majority of sessions may incorporate work with hypnosis. Whether an analysis may reasonably be called a hypnoanalysis specifically, would, I should say, depend on the hypnosis settings and the hypnotic activity having played a meaningful and significant role in the total therapeutic effort. As part of this view it must be obvious that hypnotherapeutic work may consume certain sessions almost entirely, yet only a small share of others.

The length of individual hypnoanalytic sessions may match the conventional psychoanalytic, although this can of course be altered if deemed desirable. Generally it is not changed in standard private practice interviews, and forty-five minutes is sufficient for such purposes. A lesser time is feasible for some hypnotherapeutic modifications, but usually this affords too little opportunity for pursuit of intensive analytic investigation. In some clinics and institutional arrangements it may be possible and even expedient to employ longer interviews than is customary. In the resolution of an amnesia, in a particular case, I extended sessions to one and a half and two and a half hours (Schneck, 7). For intensive, uninterrupted work in relatively circumscribed psychological areas this may be especially advantageous, but not always practicable. Such opportunities were generally unavailable for much of the work I have described on other occasions (Schneck, 8).

For the aforementioned patient with an amnesia, the lengthened sessions permitted a continuity of clinical investigation with an intensity favoring resolution of difficulties that might not have been handled as effectively in contacts of briefer duration and spread out over a longer period of time. The patient experienced strong feelings of guilt when absenting himself from his military duties. In addition to an array of pertinent, contributory, background experiences bearing on his problem, this patient was burdened by special points of identification of his wife with his mother. Aware of the weaknesses of his wife, he feared that she might duplicate the unacceptable sexual behavior of his mother, dating to his early years. This enhanced the danger of his being precipitated into the same emotional turmoil that had been part of his early development and that resulted in basic personality defects. Leaving his military duties was linked to this emotional conflict, and his memory loss was significant in relation to his sense of guilt in connection with his act, and to his need to repress the emotional impact of the distress of his childhood and adolescent years.

5. *Hypnoanalysis and the Concept of Trance Depth*

We come now to the point at which hypnotic induction is introduced into the analysis, and to general themes relating to what one strives to achieve here. One view about hypnoanalysis encountered frequently, that is in my opinion erroneous and retarding, stresses the need for the patient to attain a somnambulistic trance, or as stated in other terms, a deep trance. This is a classical concept of hypnotic involvement which I believe fails to appreciate dynamic aspects of personality functioning as would relate to the patient's utilization of the hypnotic setting. In part, the erroneous view does not imply lack of appreciation of the intricacies in personality functioning as viewed by therapists, but an earlier stage in the development of hypnoanalysis and recognition of possibilities when employing it. The specific stress in focussing on the somnambulistic state is on the ability of the patient to experience posthypnotic amnesias and to utilize techniques of regression and revivification. Under more special circumstances it would involve the ability of the patient to participate in the hypnotic state with his eyes open rather than closed, the latter usually being the case in routine procedures pertaining to hypnosis.

It is true that the ability to incorporate posthypnotic amnesias, whenever they are deemed therapeutically desirable and helpful, is a distinct advantage as long as other aptitudes are present too. But to regard this as a primary requirement for effective hypnoanalysis is misleading because many patients have been able to achieve goals successfully without ever having had occasion to demonstrate posthypnotic amnesias. Furthermore, clinical experience shows that in routine practice where special treatment settings involving meticulous and prolonged work on induction methods is the exception rather than the rule, the majority of patients do not easily adapt themselves to hypnotic behavior or do not demonstrate intrinsic aptitudes in behavior that permit the elicitation of posthypnotic amnesias on suggestion or even spontaneously. The patients who can achieve this are far fewer than the subjects encountered in psychological experimental settings, for example, or in demonstration circumstances. Among the complex mechanisms involved that account for the differences is the nature of the defenses brought into play in relation to the exposure of unconscious conflict. In routine hypnoanalytic practice, if no special effort is made to encourage the development of post-hypnotic amnesia, no more than one patient in ten, perhaps less, is likely to develop such amnesias. These figures involve amnesias that may occur spontaneously, without specific utilization of post-hypnotic suggestions to elicit them. Among patients who do not have complete amnesias, partial posthypnotic amnesias occur from time to time, in some instances as a result of posthypnotic sug-gestion and occasionally spontaneously in relation to inner needs pertaining to the dynamic significance of portions of the hypnotic sessions. The spontaneous partial posthypnotic amnesias are ap-parently more frequent than such amnesias evoked by post-hypnotic suggestion, but they may be overlooked often because the patients themselves may not be aware posthypnotically of their occurrence. Unless the content of the interview happens to come in for fairly complete discussion soon thereafter, the analyst too may not be aware of their existence.

Several hypnotic rating scales, or measurements of depth in its traditional connotation, imply that the ability of a subject to open his eyes during the hypnosis, without emerging from it as a consequence, is an attribute of a deep or somnambulistic state of hypnosis and cannot be achieved unless the subject has already demonstrated an aptitude for developing complete posthypnotic amnesias. I had occasion to point out some time ago that this view is erroneous because many subjects who may never demon-strate posthypnotic amnesias do have the ability to function with eyes open in the trance state (Schneck, 9). The accuracy of this observation is tested easily. I believe the persistence of the in-accurate view is probably associated with the hesitancy of investi-gators to evaluate such functioning during their early efforts owing to undue concern over losing control of the hypnotic relationship when the element of control as part of a transference-counter-transference issue may mean much to them. Scales of the type described carry authoritative reenforcement when they are repro-duced in books on hypnosis (10).

The ability of a patient in hypnoanalysis to open his eyes as the trance persists often goes hand in hand with freedom of move-ment and speech. Although opening of eyes under such circumstances is not always essential and may never be necessary for many patients undergoing hypnoanalysis, it has certain advantages under special circumstances. For example, if •automatic writing is employed as one of the methods in a hypnoanalysis, the patient who can open his eyes during the hypnosis is able to scrutinize his productions visually and to participate more fully this way in an assessment of his functioning (Schneck, 13). It will be noted too that automatic writing is generally regarded as an attribute of a medium trance in its classical description. There are additional advantages that have broader implications. The patient who functions in this way, even though he may not develop partial or complete posthypnotic amnesias, can participate in clinical psychological testing procedures for assisting in evaluation of personality function as part of diagnostic efforts, or in the concurrent interest in evaluating progress in treatment as reflected in projective testing devices in particular (Schneck and Kline, 11). The desirability or reliability of such measures for those purposes does not concern us here, but the fact that they are often used in this way is pertinent to the discussion. In a broader context too, subjects as described can participate in studies aimed at investigating the intricacies of personality development, and operations apart from specific treatment concerns (Schneck and Kline, 12). Several of the better known projective and evaluating techniques used in connection with hypnosis are the Rorschach Test, the Bender-Gestalt, the Thematic Apperception Test (Schneck, 14), the Wechsler-Bellevue Scale, and the Minnesota Multiphasic Personality Inventory. In addition there is the House-Tree-Person Test and varieties of figure drawings and similar measures.

The issue of hypnotic phenomena in relation to traditional concepts of trance depth is emphasized further in claims that regression, for example, is useless to attempt if the patient can achieve only a light or medium trance (15). Yet contradictory claims are made on this score (16). If the first view were accepted it would appear that by definition, perhaps, if regression is possible a deep trance exists. My own experience has been that hypnotic regression and revivification can be found in some patients who may not be able to produce posthypnotic amnesias. It is not unusual for such regressions to occur spontaneously under such circumstances in response to deep seated dynamic needs during certain phases of hypnoanalysis.

All of these observations reenforce the increasingly accepted view among hypnotherapists that the usual concept of trance depth based on descriptive phenomena alone must give way to a more psychologically dynamic view of depth in terms of emotional involvement of the patient in the trance state itself and in the psychological content of the hypnotic setting. The latter involvement may obtain even when this setting is described in traditional terms as light or medium. The hypnosis may be viewed as deep if significant emotional involvement is present.

6. Denial of Hypnosis

Denial of hypnosis is encountered frequently. It is based on the psychological need of the patient to assert such denial because of inner demands to do so, whatever their basis. Such needs may result in this denial regardless of the nature of the hypnotic experience. I have observed this in cases of patients clearly aware of the existence of partial posthypnotic amnesias, and at times in the face of complete amnesia but with recall of induction procedure. Denial is usually of more concern to the novice than to the experienced therapist as far as its implied negative impact on the hypnotic relationship is concerned, and its effect on the therapist's image of himself as participant in this therapeutic encounter.

When denial of hypnosis occurs, it is incumbent on the hypnoanalyst to decide whether treatment should proceed along hypnotic lines. This decision is prompted by his over-all clinical experience, his actual detailed knowledge of the patient at the time or inferences drawn from brief contact with him, and expressed preferences at such points by the patients themselves. One patient asked from time to time that hypnotic methods be incorporated into his treatment because he believed they might be of additional benefit to him. These requests arose despite the satisfactory progress he was making. I knew that one of his major difficulties was a considerable need to control people, and I knew too that much anxiety was stirred up when he was unable to exercise such control or when it was taken from him. There was little doubt that he would be particularly pleased to produce a battle of control with me although he would not necessarily express overtly his feelings about the outcome. After he had been in treatment some time it was felt that the risk could be taken and that he might even gain from the attempt.

The induction effort was initiated, the patient started to move into the hypnosis, and eye catalepsy was achieved. After a while, he extricated himself from the hypnosis, talked about the experience of having moved into it, changed his mind, and denied noticing any hypnotic effects. The matter was handled casually with no interest expressed in repeating the procedure. At the next session the patient wanted to have another induction. Again he moved into the hypnosis and before it was terminated he was given suggestions, without stress for any posthypnotic amnesia, that he would, after coming out of the hypnotic state, alter the position of an ash tray on my desk. I rarely have recourse to such a maneuver because it usually plays no significant role in hypnoanalytic work. But for the purpose just outlined, regarding issues of control, it seemed to be appropriate. He mentioned his awareness of the suggestions, claimed they had no effect on him, but kept looking at the ash tray, asserting he had no need to touch it. Finally, he was ready to leave at the end of the session. He looked at it again and said he was going to move it, not because it had been suggested that he do this, but simply because he wished to do so. I think this serves well enough as a particular example of one ingredient that enters into a type of denial when associated with conflict over issues of control. Thereafter, hypnosis was not employed with this patient, but he continued in treatment with this event serving simply as one of many to be utilized in understanding his problems.

Another patient presented a different issue. His complaint consisted of insomnia and difficulty in concentrating on his work because of the need to give so much thought to a girl who had broken their engagement. It was clear that more pervasive difficulties were present, but he wished to focus specifically on the use of hypnotic measures to ease the immediate problem before embarking on further explorations that might be required. On two occasions he entered hypnosis without difficulty but extricated himself from it soon thereafter and found it necessary to deny an hypnotic response. When further work was done without the use of hypnosis, he reached a point of interpreting his own reaction. He said he realized that despite his initial request, he did not want to avoid thinking about her even though it was interfering with his work and sleep. If he were successful with the hypnosis itself, he would be achieving a goal he really did not wish to reach. Plans were worked out for an approach to his problem and from that point on he was able to utilize the hypnotic procedures without difficulty.

7. Initiation of Hypnoanalysis

The question of depth and its connotations is not the only important issue for hypnotic induction in relation to the analysis. The timing of the initial induction is significant. This timing would depend on the analyst's concept of the nature and conduct of a hypnoanalysis. Robert Lindner (17), to illustrate, viewed hypnoanalysis as consisting of three phases. The first involves a period of training in hypnosis. The goal is to achieve rapid induction, response to posthypnotic suggestions, ease of recall of past memories, and utilization of regression and revivification. With daily interviews for this and succeeding phases, the training period should presumably last no longer than one week. The second phase consists of sessions involving free association in conventional fashion with introduction of hypnosis to undercut resistances. During the hypnotic setting resistances are bypassed and crucial events are recalled or reenacted. Posthypnotic amnesia is suggested and achieved. Later the events of the hypnosis are recalled by the patient during the process of free association in the waking state if the material, according to Lindner, is memorially valid. Such functioning constitutes the "interim phenomenon." The third phase of treatment is a period of reeducation and reorientation for the patient, and posthypnotic suggestions are used for reenforcement.

There are a number of questions to be raised about this view of hypnoanalysis and the discussion leads automatically into the nature of my own practice, undoubtedly overlapping also the attitudes of others. It is not clear how consistently and specifically the standard procedures were actually followed. As for the daily interviews and the systematic division into phases of treatment, it is conceivable that they may have been adhered to rigidly, or at least that an attempt may have been made to do so in institutional settings where Lindner did some of his work. The disciplined atmosphere of a correctional environment could lend itself to such standardization. The everyday events, pressures, and problems of the run of patients seeking help in private practice generally do not permit this relatively rigid, systematized, consistent relationship. Daily visits are conceivable, as they are in conventional analytic contacts, although significant changes have occurred in the frequency of this demand and in beliefs regarding its necessity. But patients are in a minority who would care to embark on the systematic training procedure advocated in this approach.

The hypnotic aptitudes regarded as necessary for treatment under the proposed plan call only for somnabules as prospective candidates for hypnoanalysis. Many patients interested in such treatment are aware of the fact that significant therapeutic work can be achieved without the necessity for somnambulistic states. Others may not wish them. And it is already the experience of a number of hypnoanalysts, as well as my personal experience, that somnambulistic levels of functioning are by no means necessary for successful work with hypnoanalysis. Furthermore, the many types of patients seeking help, with complex variations in their problems and personalities, make it highly unlikely that any such standardized technique can be pursued effectively, especially in private practice settings and in outpatient clinic settings as well. Again, the possible exception, though hard to conceive of if we allow for patient variation, is the institutional setting.

In some institutional environments with their altered milieu affecting the role of authoritative influence on prospective patients, different from the atmosphere of everyday life with its greater element of freedom and relations with authority, the ratio of somnabules to the larger group of hypnotizable subjects is higher than would otherwise obtain elsewhere. This altered ratio is suggestive of the military setting where somnambulistic functioning is found more frequently than elsewhere among psychiatric patients. The percentage of somnambules probably approximates the twenty or twenty-five per cent encountered in some psychological experimental situations or in demonstration groups. In the private practice of psychiatry the somnambules probably average no more than ten per cent, as stated elsewhere, for most hypno-analysts whose office arrangements, in terms of time schedule for length of sessions and successive appointment spacing, approxi-mate conventional standards of forty to fifty minutes, one to four or five visits per week. If the somnambulistic state is prerequisite for hypnoanalysis, the number of patients for whom it may be used would be small indeed. Fortunately for many, the conduct of a hypnoanalysis need not be predicated on this alleged essential. No doubt there are advantages to the patient who can function this way, provided he demonstrates general therapeutic abilities and flexibility necessary to insure success. It is understandable that some therapists may, from personal choice, elect to treat patients only if they fall into this category. The limitation in the number of such patients, in addition to limitations in the number of patients who demonstrate real ability to fit into the psycho-analytic framework in general, creates a situation in which there would be limited applicability for hypnoanalytic work were it not that other therapists have found, for reasons already mentioned, that these requirements can be circumvented.

One need not agree with the general view of hypnoanalysis presented by Lindner and with the idea of a training period and specific goals to be achieved before hypnoanalysis can seriously be considered. The opinion of introducing hypnotic induction very early in the contact would be shared by many, however, even though the goals in induction may not. I would say that induction should be introduced early if the patient is intent on hypnoanalysis and reluctant to accept postponement of hypnotic elements. Rarely do I utilize induction procedure during a first interview, because I feel it is important to arrive at a tentative evaluation of the patient's personality functioning in a routine encounter during which background data are obtained. A patient who is incapable of agreeing to this is generally not a good candidate for hypno-analysis, with few exceptions.

If a patient is agreeable to further exploration on a non-hypnotic level, such an approach can be additionally fruitful if only for the reason that his over-all personality functioning can be assessed further and his manner of dealing with a conventional interchange examined more closely. It is possible often to view at this time his realistic conceptions of hypnosis and hypnoanalysis, and his fantasies as well. The extent to which these issues are discussed will vary, depending on the analyst's judgment as to possible influence on resistances and on the unfolding transference relationship. For example, if a patient shows the need to control and is fearful of being controlled, some comments may be made to allay anxiety on this score. An alternative more suitable for others may be the valid representation of the hypnoanalytic setting as one wherein healthy controls will ultimately be reenforced as the need for neurotic control is relinquished. If a patient seems submissive and dependent, he may be told that the analytic work may achieve alteration in this pattern if it is felt that the patient may have considerable anxiety about the hypnotic relationship reenforcing these attributes. On the other hand, such claims may be avoided if in the judgment of the hypnoanalyst the patient must depend upon these personality needs for satisfactory initial involvement in the hypnotic interpersonal relationship, to be followed only later by an analysis of these dependency requirements. Sometimes all comment prior to induction may be avoided and the initial exposure, no less clarification of such concerns, may be made to await their reflection in the form taken by the patient's hypnotic behavior itself.

8. *Misleading Requests for Hypnoanalysis, Hypnotic Induction, and Misunderstandings about Hypnosis*

I have observed that some patients seeking hypnotherapy or hypnoanalysis do not in fact really want it. The request serves as means of establishing a psychiatric contact that had been avoided owing to hesitancies of various sorts. It is not unusual for patients desiring a change in analysts to use the request for hypnosis as a reason for effecting such transfer. The real reasons involved may never be evaluated adequately with the previous therapists. When this happens, the patient may not care whether hypnosis is actually used, he may change his mind about it, or he may lose interest soon after it is incorporated into the analytic setting. Questions about its use again may arise for some of these patients at points when strong resistances are reactivated during the course of treatment. Decisions made on this score vary with individual requirements. If the initial request for hypnoanalysis is taken at face value, the analyst may be seriously misled in evaluating the needs of his patient unless he sees through the screen soon thereafter.

During the initial hypnotic session and the several to follow, patients are given the opportunity to observe their abilities to move into a hypnotic state, to observe their reactions and experiences, to grow as initially comfortable as possible with the general hypnotic approach, to observe resistances and defenses in so far as possible at this point, and to emerge from the setting with relative ease and without discomfort. In succeeding sessions the instructions and suggestions for induction are reduced to a minimum, a simple signal for emergence is established and employed, and the main focus of attention becomes the hypnotic methods that have been presented to the patient for possible use, and their utilization for the basic work of the analysis.

It would seem to me that induction can be introduced during the initial phase or the major analytic phase of the analysis. As long as the hypnotic sessions play a meaningful role in the total investigation, the type of treatment involved is legitimately a hypnoanalysis, as discussed previously. If the main phase of treatment has been concluded and the terminal phase is in progress, the use of hypnosis would be essentially supportive and it would be questionable to categorize such therapy as hypnoanalytic.

Two frequent misconceptions about hypnosis are encountered among patients almost invariably. One is that hypnosis is basically a state of unconsciousness. The other is that all patients have posthypnotic amnesias and that such amnesias are actually a necessary attribute of the hypnotic state itself, or, as we see clinically, the broad spectrum of conditions subsumed under the heading of hypnotic state. The first misconception should be corrected easily by the obvious explanation that the patient, in hypnoanalysis, participates actively in conversational exchange with the analyst, is generally quite aware of his surroundings, is concerned about what is said and done, examines his thought processes, and scrutinizes his emotions. This type of participation cannot, therefore, be accomplished in a state of unconsciousness, especially the physiological unconsciousness of the patient's fantasy. The logical issue of confusion has to do with misunderstandings regarding the significance of the "dynamic unconscious" as opposed to other uses of the term "unconscious" and the term "unconsciousness." An explanation that a minority of patients experience complete post-hypnotic amnesias spontaneously or on suggestion should clear up the second point. Of interest, however, is the frequency with which patients allude to both misconceptions, following initial hypnotic experience, almost as if the explanations had never been given. This should not be surprising when one takes into consideration that factual misconception and logical explanation are a small part of this picture. Basically the views on hypnosis presented by patients are intimately linked with unconscious fantasies, many of which can be explored in the course of a hypnoanalysis. Such explorations can constitute an integral part of the total hypno-analytic procedure. We shall be examining some examples of such fantasies.

9. Hypnotizability, Reactions to Hypnosis, Transference and Counter-transference

During the initial induction and several subsequent hypnosis sessions within the context of hypnoanalytic therapy, the center of attention focusses, with occasional exceptions, on the patient's ability to achieve eye closure, to participate in hand levitation or some other induction procedure, to become increasingly aware of psychophysiological responses to the hypnotic setting and suggestions, to observe the over-all feeling tone of the hypnotic state as far as he personally is concerned in his involvement in it, to note variations in emotions and sensations from time to time, to experience a fair measure of relaxation, and to experiment in particular with some techniques of visual imagery. Eye closure is not essential for induction but the majority of patients achieve it. This lends itself more readily to work with visual imagery. Hand levitation is not an absolute requirement but it is often conveniently employed for initial induction purposes. If it is not used for basic induction, it can be integrated into the preliminary or later work for intensifying the feeling of "depth," or, in line with previous discussions, to further the feeling of emotional involvement in the hypnotic experience. Psychophysiological responses, awareness of feeling tone, variations in sensation and emotion, and spontaneous visual images are immediately observed and captured by some patients, whereas others suppress or repress such experience content for a variety of reasons that are linked closely with their more pervasive ways of functioning psychologically. They can be assisted in acquiring the ability to become more deeply aware of what transpires within them through direct questioning at times. Denial of awareness in the several areas of functioning may persist for a while in some rigid and coarctated patients, but the more flexible can gradually be encouraged to broaden the range and depth of their self-observations.

Many studies have been done on the question of hypnotizability and its prediction. Attempts have been made to correlate it with personality traits. Test procedures have been utilized in an effort to objectify the predictability of hypnotizability. There is no need to go into detail. One example of such investigations was published more than twenty years ago. It concerned the use of the Rorschach Test in the prediction of hypnotizability (79). It was preceded by many published papers, and numerous writings on the subject have appeared since then. Generally some minor indicators arise from such investigations and they appear to be of interest. The hypnotizability of hypnotists has been evaluated as well (80). The fact remains that for the purpose of assessing the ability of patients to enter hypnosis when hypnoanalysis is considered, the only practical approach is to move along with induction procedure, note reactions, modify efforts when required, and assess results on the basis of such trials and experience. Thus far, clinical assessments of patients by hypnoanalysts far surpass in meaningfulness, within the therapeutic setting, anything that prior testing might reveal.

Special points that arise with individual patients are more important than generalizations derived from test studies. I pointed out some time ago in connection with psychosomatic reactions to induction, that they constitute somatic expressions of anxiety associated with the hypnotic experience or defenses against it. Hypnotic experience may serve as a vague, ill-defined, intensely threatening, noxious agent that is potentially capable of overwhelming some patients, permitting the uprooting of defenses erected against the exposure of unconscious conflict (Schneck, 81). Kline has pointed out that not only may the hypnotic state itself evoke the organization of resistance patterns, but specific words used in induction may serve as stimuli for production of resistant behavior (82). It seemed that this would be particularly true where resistances are linked with sexual connotations especially. The examples given are of interest because the sexual themes parallel experiences frequently encountered in hypnoanalytic work. A twenty-four year old married woman said, "When you told me I was going deeper and deeper into a hypnotic sleep, I had a picture in my mind of myself and (a girl friend with whom she was involved homosexually) lying on a bed. I was fondling her breasts and she was going deeper and deeper into my vagina. I was very disturbed by this picture." A twenty-two year old woman revealed, "When you said my eyelids were going down, down, down—I saw myself in bed and I thought of having intercourse. The penis was going down, down, and down but it was no good— I couldn't do anything. I had failed again. I thought I was going to fail in the hypnosis too. This made me feel very angry and upset."

Sexual factors play a role frequently in the disruption of induction procedure or in reactions of discomfort during the induction process. These elements are sometimes expressed immediately and at other times are delayed. They may be revealed clearly or may be understood only after more extended analytic efforts. Usually they do not preclude continued work with hypnosis. However, in some cases they may suggest the desirability of discontinuing plans for hypnoanalysis, at least at such points, and favor non-hypnotic psychotherapy. A young woman disrupted hypnotic procedure and denied experiencing subjective changes when entering hypnosis work she had requested. The hypnotic effort had been postponed previously because of concerns about its desirability for her. She was able to reveal arousal of intense sexual feelings on induction, bordering on orgasm, and her entire history with its sexual pathology suggested the likelihood of her hypnotic reactions disrupting her equilibrium to such an extent that further hypnotic work with this pre-psychotic patient was abandoned. Another patient was proceeding well with her hypnoanalysis when she became suddenly quite uncommunicative. Exploration revealed that she identified the hypnoanalyst with someone else who in turn was linked to strong sexual associations. Her behavior was a defense against, and at the same time a revelation of her sexual impulses within the hypnotic transference. Here again, as is frequently discovered, the hypnotic setting intensified these impulses.

Transference and countertransference issues play a role, of course, in the seeking of hypnotic induction or treatment by patients and in the interest of hypnotherapists in hypnotic activities. Needless to say, there is overlapping in the satisfaction of such needs through a hypnotic setting and through non-hypnotic therapeutic activities ranging from short-term psychotherapy to lengthy psychoanalysis. Differences are present in degrees of reactions and in the complex facets of such feelings and reactions in individual patients and therapists. Meares (83), for example, mentions the neurotic, masochistic woman seeking treatment not so much for symptom relief as for the need to feel overpowered, hoping to find this in the hypnotic experience. Then there is the masculine, aggressive woman requesting hypnosis to prove she will be able to resist submitting to any man. Perverse motivations apply to hypnotherapists also, and as a result problems arise and interfere with treatment settings. It is not difficult to visualize the therapist more concerned with power drives than with the need or wish to benefit his patients. Heterosexual and homosexual features pervade the hypnotic relationship and create difficulties when the drives are insufficiently understood, or are mismanaged.

In hypnoanalysis, non-verbal cues play an important role in the hypnotic relationship whether during the induction phase or in other phases of hypnotic procedure. Certainly they are significant in non-hypnotic therapy too, including, as is acknowledged increasingly, the more traditional forms of psychoanalytic precedure. Often the implications and effects of such cues are intensified in hypnosis which tends in general to highlight issues of suggestion, not only as it is understood in its most simple aspects, but also in its complex facets. Non-verbal gestures, attitudes, and expressions carry weight, and Meares has expressed the opinion that in his experience non-verbal suggestion is of greatest importance with intelligent and critical patients who are prone to reject direct verbal suggestions (84).

I have already referred to psychosomatic reactions as well as others in response to the induction of hypnosis. In the same way that non-verbal suggestions or cues may be employed to facilitate hypnotic response, verbal stress on certain defensive reactions can be used to reenforce evidence of patient response to induction in order to further the development of as great a degree of participation in the hypnosis as possible. However, the level of the patient's anxiety must be assessed clinically. In some instances, unless this level is slight, the hypnosis should not be pushed. It can be developed in graded steps during which the patient can feel more comfortable and achieve gradual acceptance. Frequently, owing to the defensive reactions almost routinely observed in some measure in most patients, the second hypnotic induction demonstrates intensification of resistances stirred up in the initial session. Subsequent interviews generally show easing in anxiety and more comfortable hypnotic responses unless special problems exist. Restlessness, negativism, simulation, depreciation, and a variety of other behavioral features are mentioned here and have been discussed by other hypnotherapists (85).

10. Two-stage Hand Levitation Technique, and Induction Phenomena

I have found that what I have designated as a two-stage hand levitation technique for induction touches on the theme just discussed (Schneck, 86). The hand levitation method, generally more difficult for patient and doctor, is preferred by some therapists, and its elucidation and management is probably most closely associated with the method introduced by Erickson and based on ideomotor principles (102). The two-stage procedure is essentially similar except that it is initiated by having the patient deliberately lift his hand slowly for a distance of several inches, after which suggestions are given for the hand to continue to rise into the air more and more automatically so that eventually its movement is experienced as non-voluntary. I have substituted this method for the original, and for ocular fixation in almost all cases during the past few years, and believe it is quite suitable for hypnoanalysis. The patients appear to be less threatened at the outset because of their voluntary participation. The inertia frequently encountered for initial movement is eliminated. The procedure is more rapid as a result, and less wearing for patient and doctor alike. The problem of inertia accompanied by related defenses is so great at times, that I have seen some of its exponents actually initiate the hand movement themselves by placing their fingers under the patient's wrist and raising the hand themselves in this way.

The nature of methods of induction are not fundamentally important in the practice of hypnoanalysis although I imagine that with acquisition of experience, most hypnoanalysts would choose the most simple procedures and would attempt to avoid those that suggest magical operations. It is conceivable that the latter might be desirable for some patients for special reasons and when therapeutically indicated, but I doubt that this would happen often in hypnoanalytic practice. Aids to hypnotic induction may be used (88, Schneck, 87), but here again, simple verbal measures are likely to be most expeditious.

During hypnotic induction, minor conversion reactions may occur as well as psychosomatic reactions. One that I have encountered consists of the patient's inability to close his eyes despite repeated voluntary efforts and instructions to do so. Conflicts in the area of seeing and being seen with all their ramifications are clearly involved and can at times be explored. Comparable dynamic issues arise in conventional psychoanalytic settings pertaining to use of the couch and not looking at the analyst. The conversion reaction mentioned above is expressed on a neuromuscular level with a disturbance in the efficient reciprocal activities of the levator palpebrarum and the orbicularis oculi with its orbital and palpebral components or both. One of these patients manifested parallel reactions on other occasions when, for example, she related the feeling that a peculiar experience in hypnosis consisted of her body maintaining its customary position, seated in the chair facing the therapist, with her face feeling as if it had turned sideways, looking away from him. In fact it had not turned although she was not certain whether or not it had done so. On another occasion when her eyes were closed in the hypnosis she had the impression that they were partially open although she saw nothing (Schneck, 89-91).

The anxiety reflected in psychosomatic reactions, in the conversion features described here, and in other responses, plays a role of course in the frequent denial of hypnosis. Yet occasionally a patient is encountered who claims the existence of an hypnotic state when its induction has been doubtful. This is unusual in hypnoanalytic work and when it appears, treatment can continue without interruption while the issue is clarified further. During the clarification, hypnotic procedure may continue to be employed if it is deemed desirable. I have had occasion to report on a paramnesia and associated distortions relating to the alleged existence of a hypnotic state (Schneck, 92).

It will be inferred, of course, that reactions to induction and the manner in which the patient attempts to cope with this emotionally tinged encounter are directly related to complex facets of personality structure and functioning. Some patients comment directly on this when expressing concern about hypnotic performance by stressing their perfectionistic tendencies. Often, evaluation of such patients reveals less the personality configuration of the perfectionist, and more the characteristics of what I have defined as "pseudo-perfectionism" (Schneck, 93). The details have been outlined elsewhere, and I may mention in regard to hypnosis that hypnoanalytic investigations often reveal these patients to have experienced a series of failures in many areas prior to their therapeutic contacts. Their concern is hardly with precision and detail in order to insure excellent performance. Conflict over precision and detail is part of their general difficulty in managing even occasional accomplishments, no less polished proficiency. Horney (5) has stressed the characteristics of the perfectionistic type and I have pointed out some differences in points of view on this score based on my observations of pseudo-perfectionists. The presence of true perfectionism can be discerned readily enough through personality study during hypnoanalysis.

It should be evident that the mechanics of hypnotic induction are not crucial to our interest in hypnoanalysis, and with a little experience they present no problem. The personality dynamics inherent to the induction process are of basic concern in terms of what they reveal about the patient and about the hypnoanalyst too. What is learned in this way is of value in the conduct of the hypnoanalysis.

11. The Concept of Depth Reversal during Termination of the Hypnotic State

An essential parallel to patient participation in induction is present in the termination of hypnosis sessions. For all practical purposes, there is rarely any difficulty in terminating the hypnotic state. When a large body of literature is examined, however, and if inquiries are made regarding termination problems in a large variety of hypnotic settings rather than in hypnoanalysis specifically, much interesting data can be assembled. A report on the subject was rendered by Williams when he discussed difficulties in dehypnotizing (94). Problems encountered include manifestations of anxiety when hypnosis is terminated, difficulty in ending the trance, aggressive or other adverse behavioral features during termination or following it, failure to achieve eye opening on termination, and other reactions.

In hypnoanalytic work, trance termination, in its most simple aspects, should allow adequate time for patients to reorient themselves. This varies among patients. Some are capable of rapid reorientation and others require a moment or two for achieving a comfortable waking state. The time allowed and the suggestions given must be geared to the requirements of the individual. When inducing hypnosis, some patients with experience enter it within a few seconds. Others require a more prolonged induction in terms of time for proper and comfortable emotional involvement in the hypnosis. Occasionally patients are uncomfortable if induction suggestions are too time consuming. They move along more rapidly than the therapist realizes.

I have reported on what I have called "depth reversal during termination of the hypnotic state." I believe its recognition is significant in the conduct of a hypnoanalysis (Schneck, 95). Patients generally give the impression of moving smoothly and gradually from a hypnotic state to a waking state. In fact, however, many patients experience subjectively a fluctuating response. The hypnosis may deepen for them, once or more than once, between the time termination is suggested and the point of the patients' actual emergence from the hypnosis. At times the hypno-analyst may suspect this when he observes more marked head nodding, facial flattening, or body slumping when a patient is seated in the chair opposite him. Patients may mention the depth reversal spontaneously or they may reveal it in response to questions. The reversal and final emergence may take place in a matter of seconds, or in some instances the reversal may delay the point of actual termination so that a minute or more is taken up with the procedure. I believe the significance of depth reversal parallels that of depth variation in patients from session to session or within individual hypnosis sessions. Depth bears a relationship to the hypnoanalyst's instructions and to the dynamic needs of the patient at the moment. These needs are related to inner conflicts, transference relationships, and physiological states such as hunger, visceral distention, and the need for sleep. The nature of the connections between these states and the hypnotic responses varies with different patients.

Occurrences of depth reversal and its partial or complete explanations may be illustrated best by quoting patients who have experienced this happening during hypnoanalysis. One patient, for instance, mentioned the pleasure derived from the relaxed feeling in hypnosis and the wish to maintain it. For present purposes only this point will be stressed regarding the aforementioned patient, disregarding transference implications. Another patient claimed there were additional things she wanted to say before coming out of the hypnosis. The reversal was an expression of this wish. Still another patient said that there were unresolved problems she had the need to deal with before emerging from the hypnosis and this was reflected in the reversal although at the moment there was not an irresistable need to verbalize exactly what these problems were. A fourth patient referred to the depth reversal spontaneously, saying that when the signal for termination was given she wanted to continue to work on the problem in mind and to solve it. She believed that intensifying the trance state was consistent with this wish. However, closer examination of the situation revealed it to be more complex, permitting an additional inference. The topic she had in mind pertained to certain aspects of marital conflict. The issue had come up just prior to the hypnosis. It arose again at the point of termination. In the interval, during the hypnosis, other important concerns had arisen and she had been given certain instructions. It was surmised that the depth reversal associated with the need to dwell on the marital theme may have been an effort to reenforce repression of the concerns dealt with during the hypnosis and the suggestions given her at that time. For these she was to develop a posthypnotic amnesia. And in fact, she did.

Depth reversal has been observed in patients for whom the hypnotic state apparently intensified the sexual transference. I have seen it also in patients with strong dependency needs. It has been encountered when patients were observed to have achieved considerable muscular relaxation and increased hypnotic depth during periods of respite from intense involvement in emotional issues. In hypnosis many defenses are in readiness and are employed in various ways during treatment. Very frequently, patients are on guard despite satisfactory participation in hypnosis sessions. Prior to termination of particular hypnoanalytic sessions, patients may be in a relatively light stage of hypnosis. When termination is initiated, some patients, feeling less threatened by contact with their psychological conflicts then, and with the possibility of unconscious material entering a level of awareness, can let down their defenses and permit themselves to relax more completely within the hypnosis. As may be seen, depth reversal is not present in each session consistently. Its appearance is related to dynamic issues of the moment although its actual occurrence in any one patient is probably related to basic personality patterns.

The reasons for depth reversal on termination of hypnosis may be summarized briefly. It may reflect the desire of the patient to maintain the hypnotic state because of psychological satisfactions derived from it or from the hypnotic interpersonal relationship. It may reflect the wish of the patient to continue unfinished business engaged in during the hypnosis. It may indicate the relinquishing of defenses by the patient after he had been on guard against the threat of unconscious conflict. Here again, in pointing up the investigative potential of hypnoanalysis, we find that hypnotic reactions do not constitute a simple ratio response to specific instructions. It is demonstrated that hypnotic reactions are manifestations of behavior based on fluid, dynamic processes that are highly complex and consistent with the detailed fabric of human personality.

12. Flexibility on Starting a Hypnoanalysis

Visual imagery is employed in connection with recall of past memories, sharp focus on current happenings, the review of dream material, fantasies in the form of scene visualizations, hypnotic dreaming, and visualization of automatic writing without the employment at the same time of manual procedures of automatic writing (Schneck, 8, 18). During the early phase of a hypnotic relationship the patient can grow accustomed to speaking during the hypnotic state and to engage in periods of free association. He can learn to respond with associations to any given signal with a specifically focussed thought, visual image, or emotion. Posthypnotic suggestion may be introduced in connection with material for the patient to dwell on between visits for greater awareness of daydreams and fantasies, and for encouragement of nocturnal dreaming and the recall of such dreams. Effective reaction to posthypnotic suggestion does not require amnesia for the suggestions themselves. Although automatic writing and drawing, and hypnotic age regression may be brought into the hypnotic setting soon after work with hypnosis has started, I generally stress the basic visual imagery measures first. The exceptions are the patients who appear to function readily as somnambules, and in such instances the broader spectrum of technical measures may be incorporated into treatment more rapidly if the patient does not display any special resistance to this approach.

While patients perceive the need for technical methods, they are essentially concerned with their problems and anxieties, and with relief from acute discomfort as soon as possible. Because of this, few feel really reconciled to a period of waiting through testing stages in regard to introduction of techniques. The therapeutic work in terms that they can understand is expected to set in without undue delay. As a result, it is expedient to explore gradually the several methods mentioned above, without rigid insistance that everything else be deferred. Current problems and other pertinent concerns can conveniently be discussed during some parts of sessions or a few complete sessions while the hypno-analytic devices are increasingly integrated into the total thera-peutic scene. At the same time, posthypnotic suggestions encour-aging psychological work between sessions can serve as a bond between the hypnotic elements and the non-hypnotic components of the treatment situation, enhancing a holistic approach to the hypnoanalytic contact.

Much of the foregoing denotes a view of hypnoanalysis that differs from the apparently standardized format offered by Lindner. I believe the element of flexibility is an outstanding feature and that such flexibility permits a wider range of therapeutic activity. Differences from, and similarities to the foregoing may be evaluated and consulted in the work of others such as Wolberg (19), Watkins (16), and Gill and Brenman (20).

13. Resistance and Transference

Some hypnoanalysts recommend early introduction of hypnosis through a training period in order to forestall the development of resistance to it as therapy gets under way. This seems to indicate stress on the authoritative role of the analyst and its efficacy in mediating favorable hypnotic response. My own experience does not support a view regarding the absolute necessity for such early introduction of hypnosis on these grounds. Perhaps this is due to little concern over the authoritarian role, particularly because it is of doubtful need to stress it especially in hypnoanalytic work. In such work, transference reactions and phenomena are to be analyzed and whatever reaction the patient has in relation to induction is something from which the patient can potentially learn. The evaluation of whatever behavioral responses he dis-plays can be employed to further his understanding of himself. Aside from this point of view, I am mot impressed by any special difficulties that might presumably be encountered if the analyst is seen eventually as less of an authority figure than he may have appeared to be initially to the patient. This issue is far surpassed by the complex ingredients of personality function that promote and influence the nature of induction behavior. It must be re-membered too that during initial induction, even early induction, many patients display considerable resistance rather than subservience to the influence of authority.

The issue of resistance in this specific context calls attention to the theme of resistance in all its dynamic implications for psychoanalytic work in general. A frequent criticism of hypnoanalysis pertains to the claim that hypnosis is used to undercut or by-pass resistances in an effort to hasten therapeutic progress. It is said that this is contrary to the aims of psychoanalysis, the results are more superficial, and the patient fails to acquire true understanding of his functioning and his illness. Although arguments can be devised to support both sides of the question, I think the crucial point is missed by accepting the conflicting claims at face value. The undercutting of resistances has been emphasized at times (17), but I believe it is misleading to stress it. The fact is that the manifold aspects of resistance during analysis can be approached within the setting of a hypnoanalysis. Furthermore, the hypnotic setting and hypnotic methods may be employed, often very helpfully, to assist in the analysis of resistances instead of by-passing them. Often the analysis of resistances is expedited and made more incisive by the very inclusion of hypnoanalytic measures. Thus the argument regarding dilution of the analysis has no substantiation in practice if the intent of the analyst, just as would hold true in a traditional setting, is to analyze rather than circumvent resistances.

The points concerning resistance have their counterpart in the theme of transference. The idea that a positive transference is essential to induction and therapeutic progress in hypnoanalysis is superficial and erroneous. It is superficial because any transference bond is composed of ingredients with many subtle facets, in addition to which negative features may predominate without precluding hypnotizability and progress in an over-all sense. Shifting of elements with alteration of any classification of transference from positive to negative, for example, may be reflected in hypnotic behavior including reactions to induction and attitudes toward hypnosis. The continuation of hypnoanalytic effort is not impeded. Even if problems in actual hypnotizability should arise on one or more occasions, such happenings in themselves would be part of the broader hypnoanalytic work and one of its basic characteristics as far as the particular patient is concerned. Analysis of transference reactions and phenomena is obviously part of hypnoanalysis just as is true of analysis of resistances. The hypnotic relationship tends often to intensify the emotional components of analyst-patient interaction as a result of which transference features are more prominent than they may be ordinarily. This must be taken into consideration in hypnoanalytic work and the analyst must be highly attuned not only to transference but to countertransference reactions. It is probably the latter which has created difficulty for many who have shied away or turned away completely from hypnotic therapies with much intellectualizing, but with evasion of the true emotional components of their own resistances.

References

1. Burton, A.: *Case Studies in Counseling and Psychotherapy*. Englewood Cliffs, N. J., Prentice-Hall, 1959.
2. Wolff, W.: *Contemporary Psychotherapists Examine Themselves*. Springfield, Ill., Thomas, 1956.
3. Wortis, S. B.: *Psychiatric Treatment* (Proceedings of the Association for Research in Nervous and Mental Disease, 1951). Baltimore, Williams and Wilkins, 1953.
4. Horney, K.: *The Neurotic Personality of Our Time*. New York, W. W. Norton, 1937.
5. Horney, K.: *Neurosis and Human Growth*. New York, W. W. Norton, 1950.
6. Sullivan, H. S.: *Conceptions of Modern Psychiatry*. Washington, D.C., The William Alanson White Psychiatric Foundation, 1947.
7. Schneck, J. M., The hypnotic treatment of a patient with amnesia. *Psychoanal. Rev.*, *35:*171, 1948.
8. Schneck, J. M.: *Studies in Scientific Hypnosis*. Baltimore, Williams and Wilkins, 1954.
9. Schneck, J. M.: A suggested permanent modification of hypnosis scoring systems. *J. Gen. Psychol.*, *48:*83, 1953.
10. Davis, L. W., and Husband, R. W.: A study of hypnotic susceptibility in relation to personality traits. *J. Abnorm. Soc. Psychol.*, *26:*175, 1931.
11. Schneck, J. M., and Kline, M. V.: Hypnodiagnosis and evaluation of therapy in psychiatry and clinical psychology; report of a case involving the H T-P. *Brit. J. Med. Hyp.*, *2:*8, 1951.

12. Schneck, J. M., and Kline, M. V.: The H-T-P and TAT in hypno-diagnostic studies: *Brit. J. Med. Hyp*, 5:3, 1953.
13. Schneck, J. M.: Automatic writing during hypnoanalysis. *J. Gen. Psychol.*, 46:233, 1952.
14. Schneck, J. M.: Hypnoanalysis, hypnotherapy, and Card 12M of the Thematic Apperception Test. *J. Gen. Psychol.*, 44:293, 1951.
15. Wolberg, L. R.: *Medical Hypnosis*. New York, Grune and Stratton, 1948.
16. Watkins, J. G.: *Hypnotherapy of War Neuroses*. New York, Ronald Press, 1949.
17. Lindner, R. M.: *Rebel Without A Cause*. New York, Grune and Stratton, 1944.
18. Schneck, J. M.: *Hypnosis In Modern Medicine*, 3rd Edition. Springfield, Ill., Thomas, 1963.
19. Wolberg, L. R.: *Hypnoanalysis*. New York, Grune and Stratton, 1945.
20. Brenman, M., and Gill, M. M.: *Hypnotherapy*. Josiah Macy, Jr. Foundation, Review Series, Vol. 2, No. 3, 1944.
21. Schneck, J. M. (Ed.): *Hypnotherapy*. New York, Grune and Stratton, 1951.
22. Goldsmith, M.: *Franz Anton Mesmer*. Garden City, New York, Doubleday, Doran, 1934.
23. Ackerknecht, E. H.: *A Short History of Medicine*. New York, Ronald Press, 1955.
24. Frazer, J. G.: *The Golden Bough*. New York, Macmillan, 1922.
25. Schneck, J. M.: The hypnotic trance, magico-religious medicine, and primitive initiation rites. *Psychoanal. Rev.*, 41:182, 1954.
26. Rose, R.: Psi and Australian aboriginals. *J. Amer. Soc. Psychical Res.*, 46:17, 1952.
27. Schneck, J. M.: Hypnosis-death and hypnosis-rebirth concepts in relation to hypnosis theory. *J. Clin. Exp. Hyp.*, 3:40, 1955.
28. Sigerist, H. E.: *A History of Medicine*. New York, Oxford University Press, 1951, vol. 1.
29. Hull, C. L.: Hypnotism in scientific perspective. *Sci. Monthly*, 29:154, 1929.
30. Hull, C. L.: *Hypnosis and Suggestibility*. New York, D. Appleton-Century, 1933.
31. Foreau de Courmelles, F. V.: *Hypnotism*. London, George Routledge and Sons, 1891.
32. Schneck, J. M.: *A History of Psychiatry*. Springfield, Ill., Thomas, 1960.
33. Pattie, F. A.: Mesmer's medical dissertation and its debt to Mead's *De Imperio Solis ac Lunae*. *J. Hist. Med.*, 11:275, 1956.

34. Mesmer, F. A.: *Mesmerism*, by Doctor Mesmer (1779), first english translation of Mesmer's historic *Mémoire sur la decouverte du magnetisme animal*, translated by V. R. Myers, with an introductory monograph by Gilbert Frankau. London, Macdonald, 1948.

35. Schneck, J. M.: The history of electrotherapy and its correlation with Mesmer's animal magnetism. *Amer. J. Psychiat.*, *116:*463, 1959.

36. Schneck, J. M.: The first and second Husson Commissions for the study of animal magnetism. *Bull. Hist. Med.*, *27:*269, 1953.

37. Schneck, J. M.: John Elliotson, William Makepeace Thackeray, and Doctor Goodenough. *Int. J. Clin. Exp. Hyp.*, *11:*122. 1963.

38. Esdaile, J.: *Mesmerism in India and Its Application in Surgery and Medicine* (1846). Chicago, Psychic Research Company, 1902.

39. Schneck, J. M.: James Esdaile, hypnotic dreams, and hypnoanalysis. *J. Hist. Med.*, *6:*491, 1951.

40. Schneck, J. M.: Mesmerism in Henry James' *The Bostonians*, in Schneck, J. M.: *Studies in Scientific Hypnosis*. Baltimore, Williams and Wilkins, 1954.

41. Schneck, J. M.: Du Maurier's *Trilby* and modern hypnosis. See ref. 40.

42. Schneck, J. M.: A medical hypnotherapeutic addendum to the case of M. Valdemar. *Bull. Med. Libr. Ass.*, *41:*144, 1953.

43. Schneck, J. M.: Robert Browning and mesmerism. *Bull. Med. Libr. Assn.*, *44:*443, 1956.

44. Schneck, J. M.: The fantasy of hypnotic time obliteration with related literary allusions. *J. Clin. Exp. Hyp.*, *5:*172,1957.

45. Schneck, J. M.: The hypnotic state and the psychology of time. *Psychoanal. Rev.*, *44:*323, 1957.

46. Schneck, J. M.: Charcot and hypnosis (letter). *J.A.M.A.*, *176:*73, April 8, 1961.

47. Wechsler, I.: Jean-Martin Charcot, in Haymaker, W.: *Founders of Neurology*. Springfield Ill., Thomas, 1953.

48. Schneck, J. M.: Jean-Martin Charcot and the history of experimental hypnosis. *J. Hist. Med.*, *16:*297, 1961.

49. Bernheim, H.: *Suggestive Therapeutics* (1886). New York, London Book Company, 1947.

50. Guillain, G.: *J.-M. Charcot 1825-1893, Sa Vie—Son Oeuvre*. Paris, Masson et Cie, Libraires de l' Academie de Médecine, 1955. (English translation by Pearce Bailey, New York, Paul S. Hoeber, 1959.)

51. Binet, A., and Féré, C.; *Le Magnetisme Animal*. Paris, 1887. (English translation, New York, D. Appleton and Company, 1888.)

52. Freud, S.: *An Autobiographical Study*. New York, W. W. Norton, 1952.

53. Breuer, J., and Freud, S.: *Studies on Hysteria*. New York, Basic Books, 1957.
54. Schneck, J. M.: The School of the Hospital de la Charité in the history of hypnosis. *J. Hist. Med.*, *7:*271, 1952.
55. Braid, J.: *Neurology, or, the Rationale of Nervous Sleep, considered in Relation with Animal Magnetism*. London, 1843.
56. Chertok, L.: On the discovery of the cathartic method. *Int. J. Psychoanal.*, *42:*284, 1961.
57. Oberndorf, C. P.; Autobiography of Josef Breuer. *Int. J. Psycho-anal.*, *34:* part 1, 1953.
58. Kline, M. V.: Freud and hypnosis: a critical evaluation. *Brit. J. Med. Hyp.*, *4:*2, 1953.
59. Schneck, J. M.: Countertransference in Freud's rejection of hypnosis. *Am. J. Psychiat.*, *110:*928, 1954.
60. Brill, A. A.: *Introduction to The Basic Writings of Sigmund Freud*. New York, Modern Library (Random House), 1938.
61. Jones E.: *The Life and Work of Sigmund Freud*. New York, Basic Books, 1953, vol. I.
62. Ehrenwald, J.: History of psychoanalysis, in *Science and Psychoanalysis*. New York, Grune and Stratton, 1958.
63. Moll, A. *Hypnotism*. London, Walter Scott, 1890.
64. Forel, A.: *Hypnotism*. New York, Rebman, 1907.
65. Bramwell, J. M.: *Hypnotism*. London, Grant Richards, 1903.
66. Janet, P.: *The Major Symptoms of Hysteria*. New York, Macmillan, 1907.
67. Prince, M.: *The Dissociation of a Personality*. New York, Longmans, Green, 1908.
68. Sidis, B.: *The Psychology of Suggestion*. New York, D. Appleton, 1898.
69. Boring, E. G.: *A History of Experimental Psychology*. New York, Appleton-Century-Crofts, 1950.
70. Hull, C. L.: *Hypnosis and Suggestibility*. New York, D. Appleton-Century, 1933.
71. Schilder, P., and Kauders, O.: *Hypnosis*. New York, Nervous and Mental Disease Monograph Series, 1927.
72. Hadfield, J. A. Treatment by suggestion and hypno-analysis, in Miller, E.: *Neuroses in War*. New York, Macmillan, 1940.
73. Rogers, C. R.: Psychotherapy today, or where do we go from here? *Amer. J. Psychother.*, *17:*5, 1963.
74. Schneck, J. M.: Iatrochemistry, iatrophysics and iatropsychology. *Dis. Nerv. Syst.*, *22:*463, 1961.
75. Schneck, J. M.: William Alanson White on Hippolyte Bernheim: a historical note. *Int. J. Clin. Exp. Hyp.*, *10:*115, 1962.

76. White, W. A.: *The Autobiography of a Purpose*. New York, Doubleday, Doran, 1938.

77. Simmel, E.: In *Psycho-analysis and the War Neuroses*, edited by E. Jones. New York, International Psychoanalytic Press, 1921.

78. Simmel, E.: *War Neuroses*, edited by S. Lorand. New York, International University Press, 1944.

79. Brenman, M., and Reichard, S.: Use of the Rorschach Test in the prediction of hypnotizability. *Bull. Menninger Clin.*, 7:183, 1943.

80. Le Cron, L. M.: A study of the hypnotizability of hypnotists, in Schneck, J. M., Ed.: *Hypnosis and Personality*. New York, Grune and Stratton, 1951.

81. Schneck, J. M.: Psychosomatic reactions to the induction of hypnosis. *Dis. Nerv. Syst.*, 4:1, 1950.

82. Kline, M. V.: An outline of the nature of some sexual reactions to the induction of hypnosis. *Psychiat. Quart.*, *Supp. 26:*230, 1952.

83. Meares, A.: Some moral and ethical aspects of medical hypnosis. *Practitioner*, *183:*328, 1959.

84. Meares, A.: Non-verbal and extra-verbal suggestion in the induction of hypnosis. *Brit. J. Med. Hyp.*, *Summer:* 1, 1954.

85. Meares, A.: Defences against hypnosis. *Brit. J. Med. Hyp.*, *Spring:* 1, 1954.

86. Schneck, J. M.: A two-stage hand levitation technique for the induction of hypnosis. *Amer. J. Psychiat.*, *113:*839, 1957.

87. Schneck, J. M.: Apparatus supplying an auditory stimulus for the induction of hypnosis. *Dis. Nerv. Syst.*, *11:*26, 1950.

88. Kubie, L. S., and Margolin, S.: An apparatus for the use of breath sounds as a hypnogogic stimulus. *Amer. J. Psychiat.*, *100:*610, 1944.

89. Schneck, J. M.: *Studies in Scientific Hypnosis*. Baltimore, Williams and Wilkins, 1954.

90. Schneck, J. M.: Comment on a miniature conversion reaction during the induction of hypnosis. *J. Gen. Psychol.*, *47:*235, 1952.

91. Schneck, J. M.: An unusual conversion reaction during the induction of hypnosis. *J. Clin. Exp. Hyp.*, *5:*39, 1957.

92. Schneck, J. M.: Paramnesia and associated distortions relating to the existence of a hypnotic state. *Brit. J. Med. Hyp.*, *Winter:*1, 1954-1955.

93. Schneck, J. M.: Perfectionism. *Dis. Nerv. Syst.*, *22:*35, 1961.

94. Williams, G. W.: Difficulty in dehypnotizing. *J. Clin. Exp. Hyp.*, *1:*3, 1953.

95. Schneck, J. M.: Depth reversal during termination of the hypnotic state. *Psychoanal. Rev.*, *43:*506, 1956.

96. Schneck, J. M.: An outline of the development of The Society for Clinical and Experimental Hypnosis. *J. Clin. Exp. Hyp.*, *1:*2, 1953.

97. Alexander, F., and French, T. M.: *Psychoanalytic Therapy*. New York, Ronald Press, 1946.

98. Alexander, F.: *Psychoanalysis and Psychotherapy*. New York, W. W. Norton, 1956.

99. Rado, S.: *Psychoanalysis of Behavior*. New York, Grune and Stratton, 1956 and 1962, 2 vols.

100. Alexander, F.: The dynamics of psychotherapy in the light of learning theory. *Am. J. Psychiat.*, *120:*440, 1963.

101. Schneck, J. M.: *What Is Psychotherapy?* First Annual Conference, American Academy of Psychotherapists, October 20, 1956.

102. Erickson, M. H.: Historical note on the hand levitation and other ideomotor techniques. *Amer J. Clin. Hyp.*, *3:* 196, 1961.

~~Part Two~~~~~~~~~~~~~~~~~~~~~~~~~~~~~~~~

1. Hypnoanalytic Explorations

MANY WRITINGS on hypnoanalysis, as well as on hypnotherapy in its broader aspects, stress the hypnotic setting as expeditious for the revival of buried memories. There is an element of validity in this view, but unfortunately the claim assumes a primary rather than secondary position. It is true that such memories are often clarified. But it is also true that they are often of less significance in the total treatment effort than is expected by the patient and analyst alike. Both may be puzzled, consequently, when the uprooting fails to be as significant as had been wished. Patients emphasizing this role of hypnoanalysis fail to appreciate the more involved aims and necessities of treatment. This enhances the likelihood of failure. The analyst, furthermore, is restricted in employing hypnoanalytic methods fruitfully for broader issues of concern by placing too much energy and attention on memory features. The revival of buried memories has a dramatic appeal for most patients and many therapists and this plays a role in its overemphasis.

It may be stated parenthetically, apart from current concerns with psychoanalysis and hypnoanalysis, that the possible role and influence of buried memories in illness has been a subject of interest for physicians for quite a long time. A pertinent illustration is that of the well known physician and pioneer psychiatrist, Benjamin Rush, who alluded to this issue in his famous textbook, *Medical Inquiries and Observations Upon the Diseases of the Mind*, published in 1812 (27, Schneck, 28).

The hypnotic setting can serve most constructively to assist in the elucidation of patterns of thinking, feeling, and behavior, and in focussing attention on psychological defense mechanisms (Schneck, 1). In so far as the hypnotic state fosters increased relaxation, many patients appear capable of verbalizing more

51

freely and productively (Schneck, 26). The relaxation, however, is not essential for such productiveness, because the latter may reveal itself also in the midst of varying degrees of anxiety relating to the dynamic aspects of the patient's functioning and the work at hand. The alterations in mental activity, whether subtle or gross, foster a greater ability in patients to become aware of preconscious and unconscious aspects of their total experience. For patients requiring the need to become more conscious of unconscious activity and determinants, as is generally regarded to be necessary in much of psychoanalytic effort, it is the hypnotic setting that can so often help in the promotion of these ends.

2. Hypnosis, Hypnoanalysis, and Psychological Test Methods

Some of these points of view have been illustrated in explorations involving psychological test techniques, supplementing clinical findings. It was possible to evaluate the influence of the hypnotic state on affectivity and ideation as reflected in the psychological test settings. One example consisted of House-Tree-Person drawings as a projective technique. Four subjects were presented with the H-T-P task which was then administered a second time with identical instructions. It was the same method that has been used with other subjects who were given the H-T-P test during the waking and the hypnotic states. In the dual waking procedure, three of the subjects were patients who had been in psychotherapy. The fourth had not been in treatment. There were some graphic differences in the second series of drawings in all instances. Psychological analysis revealed in the case of the dual waking administrations that the psychodynamic content of both seemed to agree essentially. A psychologist, other than the one who evaluated the results initially, arrived at the same conclusion independently. These results were compared with those of patients who had been given the H-T-P test in the waking and hypnotic states. In the latter case there were not only simple graphic differences in the drawings under hypnosis. There were significant changes in psychodynamic content. The element of hypnosis in this setting appeared to be the responsible factor rather than the element of repetition of the procedure as was the case in the dual waking administrations. The details of the case data and the drawings are available in the publication that I co-authored with Kline (Schneck and Kline, 2).

Studies were done, on patients in treatment settings, employing the H-T-P and TAT. The H-T-P was given prior to treatment. After some time had been spent in therapy the test was repeated in a waking administration, followed by testing in the hypnotic state. Then the Thematic Apperception Test records were obtained in the waking and hypnotic states. In the waking H-T-P records given after treatment had been initiated, there were reflections of apparent therapeutic gain in evidences of lessened anxiety, better organized defenses, less preoccupation with control over impulses, and increasing clarification on a conscious level of personality difficulties. The effect of hypnosis on the records was to emphasize preconscious impulses, to point up ego defenses as less effective, and to demonstrate increased perceptiveness for unconscious stimuli. Drives and suppressed associations were produced in sharper focus under hypnosis. Changes in TAT stories in hypnosis as compared to the waking material were consistent with H-T-P results and showed alterations in depth and consistency of ego defenses. These and other studies pointed up the potential assistance that the use of hypnosis could offer in more complete evaluations of personality changes during and after treatment whether or not hypnosis were used during treatment (Schneck and Kline, 3).

For a detailed and meaningful evaluation of the psychological test studies it is desirable to consult the original publications. It should be of interest, however, to highlight briefly the tone and content of some responses in order to approach this area of practice more specifically. For this purpose, TAT responses will be used.

Here is a waking reaction to Card 1 of the TAT, the boy with the violin. "There was a little boy who was very deeply attached to his father and his father died. He had spent much time listening to his father play the violin and had been very happy at those times. About a month after his father had died he took the violin down from the closet shelf and put it on the table on top of a music sheet that his father had played from. He sat there—in the picture here he's sitting and looking at the violin and thinking—

thinking of the pleasant times he had had with his father, at which point—at the end of which he decided to study violin and perhaps recapture some of the joy he had with his father. That was the result."

The patient was a thirty-two year old woman, anxious and depressed, with many fears and compulsions, disturbed over an extra-marital relationship, and giving the impression that she was verging on a psychotic collapse. Her TAT story under hypnosis was as follows: "This boy's father had died. Previous to that he'd spent much time listening to him play the violin. He (pause) he hadn't liked his father and he pulled the violin down from the closet one day to look at it and he was thinking that he was happy that he was dead—after which he broke the violin."

The approach to treatment of this patient points up a type of experience encountered in hypnoanalytic and more traditional psychoanalytic effort. An initial hypnotherapeutic involvement had as its purpose the restoration of faltering defenses, allaying anxiety, and reenforcement of ego strength. Then, in keeping with progress achieved, hypnoanalytic work was instituted. This course of action proved helpful, and the patient was able to acquire meaningful gains.

Another patient complained of chronic fatigue and depression. She suffered from nightmares, regarded herself as overemotional, and was critical of her hostile feelings toward others. This twenty-nine year old woman entered hypnoanalysis, and the psychological testing of which the following was a part, took place after eighteen sessions of treatment. At the time of retesting she was especially concerned about obstacles to progress occasioned by rigid, compulsive attributes of her husband, believing they were interfering with possibilities for working out a satisfactory marital relationship.

This patient's waking story in reaction to Thematic Apperception Test Card 1 was: "This little boy perhaps has been presented with a new violin. He may be on the verge of taking his first music lesson. He is studying the violin very intently and looking at it very carefully. His expression is one of deep interest and a certain amount of sincerity. He undoubtedly will make a good student of the violin and enjoy the ultimate success of his studies." Her hypnosis story was: "This boy has finished a music lesson. He's thinking a great deal about that lesson. He's very, very discouraged. He doesn't think he'll ever learn to play as he would like to be able to do. He doesn't know where to turn. If someone doesn't help him he'll smash the violin."

There have been other studies to evaluate the impact of the hypnotic state on mental functioning. For example, an evaluation of the word association procedure was attempted with Kline, based on earlier studies of this psychological device (4-6). Because of the special features centering around the use of hypnosis, a number of modifications were introduced into the method of administration. Stimulus words were also geared to the therapeutic interest present in this investigation. Subjects consisted of patients and university students who had not been in treatment (Kline and Schneck, 7). It was found that when hypnosis was used in the testing situation, the patterns of response among patients and non-patients showed similar trends although variation was more pronounced in the patient group. Associative alterations markedly increased in the hypnotic administration. In the hypnotic administration there was an increase in the percentage of fast reaction times and a decrease in slow reaction times. Again in the hypnotic administration the percentage of serious disturbances to traumatic stimuli increased for the patient and the non-patient groups. We were concerned with the use of the word association method in therapeutic settings and the findings pointed to the potential helpfulness of the device within the framework of hypnotherapy and hypnoanalysis. The fact that some of the subjects were already in treatment permitted a view of the potentialities which might not otherwise have been so readily discernible.

Some information will be offered now about the subjects in the patient category because they furnish a brief view of problems presented by those who enter hypnoanalysis. An eighteen year old student had problems in achievement at school and experienced much anxiety because of poor grades. He centered practically all of his concern on the school issue until he became more and more aware of deep-seated sexual conflicts. A twenty year old woman entered hypnoanalysis because of frigidity and avoidance of sexual relationships for several months. As she became increasingly aware of herself with unfolding of developmental insights, it was obvious that various interpersonal relations required rectification. A thirty-four year old woman started her hypnoanalysis when she realized that the problems of her children might be related intimately to her own psychological conflicts. She was confused about her sexual interests and drives, experienced difficulties in managing her finances, and was hazy about various goals in life. Past experiences suggested the importance in her of unconscious homosexual conflict. Such conflict obtained also for a twenty-four year old man who sought hypnoanalysis with problems of excessive dependency and feelings of inferiority. A young man of nineteen started hypnotherapy with complaints of compulsive eating, markedly mixed feelings toward his mother, and a concern over his body appearance with what he felt were its implications of femininity.

The studies mentioned above were conducted within the setting of mental health clinics. It was within this framework that patients entered hypnotherapy and hypnoanalysis. There were obvious conveniences for integrating psychological test procedures into the therapeutic regime. As far as the issue of hypnoanalysis is concerned, I should say that its conduct was essentially comparable to the work done in private practice. Procedures, interest, and orientation were similar. Of course in the clinic set-up, there is always the concern about waiting lists and related administrative problems, but the technical issues of importance in the present account remain basically parallel. This pertains specifically, for example, to patient selection and therapeutic management.

3. Hypnoanalysis, Transference, and Problems of Symptom Relief

In all types of therapeutic settings, including private practice and mental health clinics as mentioned above, patients present a wide variety of symptom complaints. Hypnoanalysts approach this problem in ways that vary with their views about symptom removal and relief and their evaluations of the best interests of the patients. Usually no attempt is made to focus attention only on the symptom. To do so would be quite inconsistent with the purposes of hypnoanalysis, the goal of which calls for more extensive personality evaluation and change. During the more involved personality explorations, however, attempts are made to gain greater understandings of specific symptoms, symptom formation, and the dynamic significances of symptoms in maintaining neurotic equilibrium.

Some patients who find their symptoms very distressing, to a point where preliminary attempt at alleviation is claimed to be necessary, may be unable to follow through with a hypnoanalysis in its greater complexities before a measure of relief is achieved. I have had occasion to point out elsewhere that for symptom relief or removal some therapists have claimed excellent results whereas others insist such efforts are quite ineffective. I have ventured the opinion that both assertions are probably exaggerations (Schneck, 8). Furthermore, the professional opposition to direct symptom removal often implies that the hypnotic efforts toward this end are simple but ill-advised. I believe this claim is far from true. It would appear, on the contrary, that symptoms essential for maintenance of psychological equilibrium will not be eliminated with ease regardless of how neurotic the equilibrium may be. It would be only fair to say that regardless of theoretical orientation, long-term psychotherapeutic and analytic efforts may be helpful in promoting favorable personality change while specific symptoms stubbornly persist. I have suggested that the disparaging view of attempts to relieve symptoms and the cavalier attitude toward their importance or persistence involves, frequently, a face saving device based on the problems in dealing with them effectively. Indeed the view of symptom relief as easy but undesirable is hardly tenable because such relief or removal is, on the contrary, frequently quite difficult to achieve.

Much is made of the recurrence of symptoms following relief, or of the substitution by new symptoms. Such reference invariably singles out hypnotherapy as the treatment setting for these happenings. As a matter of fact it would be only honest to acknowledge the easing and exacerbation of symptoms as a component of many forms of therapy including traditional psychoanalysis. This applies also to replacement of one symptom by another. Many patients with such difficulties eventually seek hypnoanalysis and by this time the symptoms themselves and the related neurotic difficulties have become firmly embedded in total personality functioning, considerably compounding the difficulties in achieving relief. As far as symptom disappearance is concerned, one may say that symptoms may be eliminated permanently with greater ease if they have played a relatively minor role in the psychological functioning of a patient with good ego strength and flexible and effective adaptive capacities. If such capacities are not very effective or flexible and if ego strength is poor, permanent relief is less likely to be achieved. Recurrence, or spontaneous symptom substitution may be expected in such cases if the symptom has been even temporarily eliminated. In attempts to alleviate symptoms, if compensatory mechanisms are ineffective the efforts themselves would be unproductive. Unless significant personality growth can come about it would make no difference whether treatment were short-term or long-term, or whether or not it involved hypnotic settings and methods. If pressure tactics are employed to force disappearance of symptoms regardless of personality needs and the level of ego strength or weakness, the procedure is clearly questionable regardless of technique, hypnotic or non-hypnotic, or theoretical orientation.

Whether or not symptom relief is effective, when technically simple measures are used the results will depend significantly on the nature of the transference relationship. This relationship serves in effect as a stimulus bearing on the personality of the patient, and at times it may set in motion a series of changes within the patient that lead to beneficial alterations. The permanent or transitory nature of personality changes will depend, at least in part, on the nature of this interaction. If effective adaptive mechanisms can be brought into play, good results may persist. Technical procedures may be remarkably similar for several therapists, but the impact of the transference will be important in determining the nature and persistence of change in the patient in accordance with the transference as stimulus. It has long been known among therapists willing to see and to acknowledge it, that beneficial changes of the order just outlined can persist and at times be followed by more pervasive personality growth. From time to time it would be reported by hypnotherapists. It is only relatively recently, with increasing interest in short-term therapy, that this view has been reactivated with an impression that it is virtually a recent discovery. The theme of meaningful change in short-term contact has, for example, been pointed up by Alexander (9).

In hypnoanalysis, it is observed sometimes that with therapeutic emphasis on one symptom and its alleviation, additional symptoms are also relieved although no special attention has been given them. It may be inferred that the underlying dynamic core is similar, and with its resolution there is an alteration in all associated components. This effect may be observed in various types of hypnotherapy and in non-hypnotic psychotherapy as well. No doubt it is the same mechanism that plays a role in symptom disappearance that occurs spontaneously, without any type of psychotherapy. Substitute symptoms may appear if, as mentioned earlier, adaptation is not achieved. The basic theme as observed clinically is, I believe, substantiated by some of the experimental work of Seitz (10).

The role of the therapist as authority and its implications for the patient in respect to therapeutic change or absence of change is surely very important. It is largely the fantasy of his role that is significant for the patient and it influences choice of therapists or changes made from one to another. This holds true in traditional analysis, hypnoanalysis and any other type of psychotherapeutic and general medical contact. It obtains also in general life settings and influences personality functioning and personality growth too. Authoritative opinion serves the function of psychological stimulus. Search for authority and authority substitution are related undoubtedly to early childhood conditionings. I have offered the opinion that pervasive needs involving this search and the need for repetitious substitutions seems to imply total functioning fixated at infantile levels. Yet the need for authority substitution may appear occasionally to serve as a special stimulus at certain turning points in the functioning of a more mature ego. The processes involved in these operations are usually essentially unconscious, yet the need may at times be expressed on a conscious level.

Sometimes the features of this functioning stand out clearly in brief hypnotherapeutic contacts. For example, a young married woman sought help for gastrointestinal discomfort which persisted long after other somatic complaints associated with a previous infectious illness had disappeared. She surmised that psychological factors were involved in the continuing symptom and conjectured its relationship to a diagnosis of anxiety neurosis that had previously been made and which had upset her. Various additional facets to this problem will be omitted here. The patient regarded herself as a suggestible person and believed that brief hypnotherapeutic effort with its authoritative connotation might suffice to restore her feelings of well being although she acknowledged the reservations that might exist, the possibility of failure, and the fact that more extensive therapy might have to be considered. Symptom relief of a lasting nature was possible here within two sessions (there were subsequent check-up interviews). Evidently the adaptive capacities discussed earlier could be exercised fruitfully by this patient, but I should regard her as one of a minority who can benefit in this way. The involved personality difficulties of most patients, seeking if not demanding short-term hypnotherapy for symptom relief without reasonable personality exploration, doom such efforts to failure. There are some theoretical considerations relating to success and failure of hypnotherapy, on a short-term basis with emphasis on authoritative influence, which will be discussed later. In any case, conscious and unconscious elements play a role in the selection of a particular therapist and in the fantasies about him, whether or not such therapy is analytic or non-analytic and whether or not it incorporates the use of hypnotic methods.

4. Hypnosis and a Concept of Attitude toward Suggestibility

The search for symptom relief in one or two hypnotherapeutic sessions is widespread at present. In most cases the requests as unrealistic expressions of unconscious needs and fantasies seeking immediate gratification, should be recognized for what they are. Efforts to have patients see their requests as unrealistic are often unsuccessful.

The point of special interest raised by the foregoing concerns is the issue of suggestibility. This cannot be brushed aside in its role during all types of therapeutic encounters, hypnoanalytic and conventional psychoanalytic as well. Regarding the hypnotic relationships specifically, it is invariably an item for discussion. Curiously, as far as hypnotizability is concerned, there is often disagreement on the score of difficulty or ease with which hysterical subjects, for example, can be hypnotized (11). If they are regarded, as is so often the case, as being especially suggestible, presumably the inductions should be simple. Often the reverse experience is encountered. My experience indicates that the degree of suggestibility is not alone the primary consideration. The significant issue is the reaction of the patient to conscious and unconscious awareness of his suggestibility and his willingness or need to accept or to reject this facet of his personality functioning. He may be unable to achieve a hypnotic state or he may experience much anxiety in the process of doing so if his tendency is to reject his suggestibility. He may show negativistic tendencies in the process. These patterns may appear during any phase of the hypnotic setting, its termination, and in posthypnotic attitudes and responses. On the other hand, if the patient is accepting of his suggestibility as a personality attribute, he may be able to adapt himself easily and smoothly to the hypnotic setting in all its complex manifestations and benefit thereby. In assessing this point of view, one must allow for quantitative as well as qualitative variations plus the additional involvement of complex interacting personality ingredients (Schneck, 8).

When suggestions are offered for symptom relief or for any other purpose in hypnotic explorations or integration, they must be carefully worded in keeping with known or inferred needs of patients based on preliminary studies of their personalities or clinical assessments emerging from the therapeutic interviews. These basic impressions will influence manner and tone, points of stress, and choice of words. They will affect ability to capitalize on known or inferred strivings of the patients.

5. Transference, Symptom Alleviation, and Hypnoanalysis

Again, with reference to specific symptoms within the broader framework of a hypnoanalysis, it should be pointed out that the ability to deal with them favorably would depend on many variables. They may be evaluated and eased early in treatment, or they may have to await more involved unfolding of personality patterns. For example, if one were to consider phobic reactions it should be pointed out that the duration of treatment and extent of personality evaluation would depend on various components.

These pertain to the type of phobia, the general personality of the patient, the dynamic importance of the symptom as an expression of intrapsychic conflict, the role of repressed memories, the ease or difficulty in retrieving and elucidating such memories, the involvements of the phobia with other symptoms and its complex relationships with the character structure of the patient (Schneck, 21).

At times a specific symptom, such as a phobia, may be capable of investigation and relief relatively early in treatment (Schneck, 22). Often such efforts require preliminary passage of time during which much more need be learned about the personality functioning of the patient (Schneck, 12). The hypnoanalyst must be aware constantly of the operations of the transference in such endeavors. Whether it is necessary to capitalize on the unanalyzed transference involvements at such times or to attempt an analysis of the transference cannot be stated categorically. Assuming that treatment will continue beyond the point of symptom relief, transference analysis need not play a role if not deemed necessary when the symptom is evaluated early in treatment. A return to appropriate transference issues can be achieved later when they may have more significance and impact. Yet some patients require for good progress that transference relationships be evaluated quite early. Indeed, this may at times be essential for good results.

Occasionally patients are encountered with problems for which background data are readily supplied in a way that suggests the significant psychodynamics (Schneck, 23). The impression is obtained that were the patient able to view the information in proper perspective, the pattern may be evident to him and the problem resolved. At times the surface simplicity can be deceiving. There have been cases, however, where the hypnoanalytic setting has been introduced permitting integration and reorganization that were apparently not possible in non-hypnotic interviews. In these instances the ability of the hypnoanalyst to infer the significant patterns early in the therapeutic relationship permits the introduction of special hypnotic methods geared to highlight meaningful aspects of the problem in a relatively short period of time. Needless to say, the fortunate preliminary inference and the availability of hypnotic methods are not enough. A broad knowledge of psychodynamics with awareness of the role of anxiety and resistance as well as the importance of transference features, and experience that controls the utilization of interpretations or their avoidance, are essentials for the proper conduct of therapy. At the core of such therapeutic efforts is the ability to apply well the principles of psychotherapy within the hypnoanalytic setting (Schneck, 12). Flexibility in efforts is important because original inferences may remain unsubstantiated, resistances of various types may not have been anticipated, and significant levels of anxiety may have been underestimated.

6. Spontaneous Sensory and Motor Phenomena

In hypnotic settings, including hypnoanalytic procedures, subjects and patients may experience spontaneously a variety of sensory and motor phenomena. They may easily and at times unfortunately be by-passed, but they are often worth exploring because of therapeutic significance. The analysis of such phenomena may at times be of incidental concern. Yet often they may prove very helpful for understanding the patient. Their analysis may also influence the direction of treatment and the time that it takes. Such phenomena, therefore, should never be regarded as basically inconsequential and fortuitous even when they are not immediately understood (Schneck, 13-15).

Spontaneous sensory and motor phenomena occur frequently. One patient had the tendency of placing her left hand to the left occipital area during the induction of hypnosis over a series of sessions. On analysis, this movement was shown to be correlated with concurrent attempts to fathom and work through her relationship with a younger sister. The position assumed by her arm became linked memorially with her being tugged by an adult in settings involving her sister, as a result of which her arm assumed a position like that in the hypnotic situations. Condensed into the psychological framework symbolized by this peculiar motor activity were a complex array of events, feelings, and fine points in early childhood relationships which blossomed into awareness and constituted an important phase of the analysis.

A young man experienced functional paraplegia with numbness and pain during several hypnosis interviews. An evaluation through concurrent verbalizations revealed that these phenomena were expressions of defense against aggressive impulses directed toward his father especially. Also involved here were feelings of guilt and punishment. The happenings could be connected directly to oedipal conflict. On a particular occasion, during a hypnosis interview, he was given suggestions for reliving his feelings about his father. His immediate reaction was to exclaim, "I can't think! I can't move my legs!" The problem had many ramifications, and various identifications and displacements directly related to this theme were uncovered.

Another patient repetitively experienced equilibrium disturbance described as a feeling as if her head were spinning. They were discovered to be associated with sensations she had had on occasions in sexual intercourse. The sensations during the hypnoanalysis were found to reflect the sexual impulses she experienced in the transference relationship. The equilibrium disturbance occurred in hypnosis at certain points when she was aware of an impulse to say something with a concurrent attempt to counteract that impulse. This was associated with relinquishing control and yielding. The hypnoanalyst was identified with several other figures with whom the patient had direct and indirect sexual involvements.

The sensation of one hand becoming very small and disintegrating was revealed by an alcoholic patient. It was mentioned during the first hypnosis and analyzed later as reflecting feelings of castration connected with his identification of the therapist with his father. Some hypnotic verbalizations that are of interest in connection with his hand getting smaller are, "My will was getting smaller, my resistance was getting weaker, my strength was going away. . .as though I was a child all over again—weakness, smallness, no strength, disintegration perhaps, not feeling up to the next person. . .a feeling of being smaller than the next person."

For a period of time during her hypnoanalysis, a patient was able to work effectively on some problems within the hypnotic setting but could not speak during the hypnosis. Analysis of this tendency revealed that the hypnotic state involved intensification of her sexual feelings toward the analyst, and the speech inhibition constituted a defense against revealing herself in this way. Ego controls were more effective in relation to these emotions when hypnosis was not used, and verbalization was not impaired.

Occasionally, sexualization of the hypnotic relationship may be so intense as to interfere considerably with any effective use of hypnosis for a period of time at least. In such cases it may be deemed advisable to avoid the use of hypnosis completely in order to forestall potential complications. A prepsychotic patient, for whom hypnotherapy was being considered tentatively, experienced intense sexual feelings during induction. They were revealed only on questioning when this was suspected, and, as a matter of fact the conflict in connection with them was expressed in her need to deny her hypnotizability completely. Similar reactions in other patients have demonstrated on occasion the existence not only of general resistance to treatment, as part of the significance of these experiences, but strong sadomasochistic components in the personalities of such patients.

A young man noticed, during certain hypnosis sessions, an equilibrium disturbance that involved a sensation of swinging back and forth. This could be traced to childhood episodes including sexual feelings involving his parents. In addition, he experienced the feeling of facing in the direction of the therapist when he was not, in fact, doing so. The combination of reactions were evaluated in the hypnoanalysis as indicative of certain homosexual components in the transference relationship.

The peculiar sensations of body positions and directions of facing, that are inconsistent with actual positions of body in space, do make their appearance from time to time. For example, a young woman with an obesity problem was clearly ambivalent about treatment and manifested resistances in various forms. She described, during one hypnosis session in particular, the odd feeling of facing the therapist directly as far as her head was concerned. Yet the remainder of her body felt reversed, one hundred and eighty degrees, in the direction of the door behind her. There was little question, confirmed later in treatment, about this phenomenon representing her mixed feelings about seeking help.

Another patient's latent homosexuality was reflected in a spontaneous hypnotic sensation of her body being very rigid and suspended in air. She also expressed at times a lopsided feeling in hypnosis which reflected her view of her own personality. In an attempt to master the expression of sexual feelings in the transference relationship she developed chills with body shaking and teeth chattering. This constituted a representation by the opposite. Sensations of chilliness to counteract and control deeper feelings of personal warmth, against the expression of which the patient attempts to guard himself, are not uncommon.

During her hypnoanalysis a patient experienced spontaneously the feeling of her entire body growing larger and swollen. It was possible for her to analyze these reactions as the somatic representation of her identification with her father. It had implications regarding certain aspects of her masculine identification from a broader point of view. "I have a peculiar feeling. I feel right now as if I've swelled up to about ten times my proportions. My body feels heavy, a swollen, heavy feeling, just as if I've swelled up past anything you can believe anyone can be." Her father, when she was a child, had always seemed so "tremendous" to her.

Some aspects of the phenomena just described have been discussed by Brenman, Gill, and Hacker as alterations in the state of the ego (16). The therapeutic implications of these alterations for some patients were implied but not described. I have pointed to these features elsewhere (Schneck, 12). The aforementioned investigators referred to the fluidity and considerable variability in the phenomena to a degree not usually encountered in the normal waking ego. I concur in this and may comment on an additional point. The phenomena at hand reflect unconscious forces in operation and, as I have mentioned earlier, can contribute meaningfully to an analysis when studied further. At the same time that the occurrences reflect and reveal hidden issues, they serve to disguise. If the threat to the patient is sufficiently great at any one point, the awareness of these peculiar manifestations may itself be repressed or suppressed so their very existence may be elicited only through questioning and other explorations. It may well be suspected that similar repression and suppression takes place also as part of the functioning of the normal waking ego. For the latter, the extent and complexity of these involvements is little recognized and understood at present.

Less frequent types of sensory and motor happenings seem to fall into the category of phenomena apparently related to bilaterality (Schneck, 60). A patient, lying with his hands on his stomach, was told his right arm and hand would move automatically and come to rest on the couch. His hand would reach the couch only when he felt deeply involved in the hypnosis. This was achieved. Immediately thereafter he repeated the maneuver spontaneously, and in the absence of instructions, with his left hand and arm. Another patient was enaged in a hand levitation procedure with his right arm, and this involved too a feeling of numbness in that arm. As soon as this was acomplished, he found to his surprise and interest, and without being able to account for it, that his left hand and arm spontaneously duplicated this sensory and motor experience.

These occurrences may be related to the work of Ames who pointed out that bilateral behavior varies in degree and type during the individual's development (61). It varies from age to age and in different children. Definite periods of unilateral arm behavior tend to alternate with periods of bilateral behavior in the infant and pre-school child in response to stimulus objects. Noteworthy periods of bilaterality were said to occur normatively at twenty-four weeks and thirty-two weeks. Alternating unilateral and bilateral behavior takes place apart from postural orientation. From four and a half to ten years of age there is little bilateral behavior.

The occurrence of bilaterality during hypnotic settings would appear to be consistent with the tendency toward regression in varying degrees, depending upon dynamic forces within patients at the time of the hypnotic settings. Evidence of spontaneous regressions and discussions of them are taken up elsewhere. Hypnosis as regression has been taken up by many investigators and in this volume I point up my own concern with hypnosis in relation to a more total phylogenetic regression. The bilaterality as a form of spontaneous sensory and motor phenomenon does seem to be part of a spontaneous regression within certain limits and probably related peculiarly to the developmental features of the particular subjects or patients. It would be hard to say for the examples given here that they definitely can be understood within the framework of the concept of regression in the service of the ego although other examples of spontaneous regression discussed here within the context of psychodynamic evaluations do serve to illustrate this point of view (48, 62, 63).

Spontaneous sensory and motor phenomena during hypnosis so often reflect transference issues. Repressive forces may be so intense that they blot out not only specific aspects of hypnotic experience but necessitate denial of the hypnosis itself (Schneck, 12). Early in his hypnoanalysis, a patient described participation in a hypnotic induction elsewhere. He regarded it as unsuccessful despite some evidence to the contrary. Again he viewed his initial experience with hypnotic induction in the hypnoanalysis now as unsuccessful despite certain hypnotic experiences such as sensory alterations including heaviness in his limbs and motor changes involving difficulty in lifting his leg from the floor. Not only did he describe his leg later as having "felt as heavy as lead," but he added details of feeling relaxed with the sensation of "going into a whirlpool." Also he lost awareness of his hands below the wrists, as if "they were not there." Additional associations and recollections highlighted recurrent dreams explicitly depicting castration anxiety (trying to avoid a dog attempting to bite off his penis), and masochistic fantasies. Analysis revealed early his denial of hypnosis implying in part a denial of femininity in his fantasy of the hypnotic relationships, and a denial of homosexuality specifically.

I have encountered not infrequently this unconscious identification of hypnosis with homosexuality. The sexual meanings of hypnosis have been of concern to a number of investigators, but so often their analyses and studies have occurred subsequent to non-analytic hypnotherapy. I believe there are many opportunities for such evaluations in the course of analytic work involving hypnosis, and hypnoanalysis is specifically well geared for these efforts. In such work it has been shown that analysis of transference relationships, including specific sexual components such as the homosexual as just mentioned, need not interfere with hypnotizability and fruitful continuation and effectiveness of the hypnoanalysis as a whole.

Retrospective views of the sexual implications of hypnosis were offered some time ago by Freud and Ferenczi among others. Freud saw the hypnotic contact as the devotion of someone in love to an unlimited degree, but here the sexual satisfaction is excluded. It differed, he felt, from being in love where this satisfaction is withheld only temporarily, remaining in the background as a possible aim later on. "Hypnosis resembles being in love in being limited to these two persons, but it is based entirely upon sexual tendencies that are inhibited in their aims and substitute the object for the ego ideal" (17). The views of Freud, Ferenczi (18), Speyer and Stokvis (19), and Schilder and Kauders (20), are part of the psychoanalytic interpretation of hypnosis with special reference to its sexual implications.

7. Theories of Hypnosis, the Nature of Hypnosis, and a Proposed Phylogenetic Conception of Hypnosis

Needless to say, the hypnoanlyst is much concerned with transference elements in the hypnotic setting and with many aspects of the trance relationship. He observes trance behavior in its most subtle forms and at times he is faced with gross manifestitations of trance expression that cannot help but be noticed. For example, I had in treatment a patient who assumed an extreme posture in hypnosis, one taken spontaneously by him on induction (Schneck, 29). When seated in his chair, he curved his head, neck, and upper body far forward. He eventually assumed a position with his head turned inward toward his body at the level of his lower abdomen or pubis. The action is intrinsically part of the variety of spontaneous sensory and motion phenomena discussed in this volume. This action continued through a series of sessions and expressed various transference issues. Some included passive submission and homosexuality, subservience and exhibitionism. I might note parenthetically that this body position was a reminder of an historical fact too. In centuries past a sect known as Hesychasts in the Greek church used the umbilicus as a focal point for trance induction. They were known also as omphalopsychics and Moll referred to them in his classic work (11).

Transference, sexual elements especially and other facets of the hypnotic interpersonal contact tend to receive special attention in psychoanalytic writings pertaining to hypnosis and their importance is not questioned. It is to be noted further, however, that they are often treated not only as special features of hypnosis but are said to account for the very nature of hypnosis. Thus, they have theoretical as well as clinical significance. Speaking of this subject, for example, Robert Lindner (30) tells of the concept of transference in the relationship between hypnoanalyst and patient and refers to it as "the relationship that allows hypnosis and actually permits the treatment to be carried out." Then he goes on to speak of points which have been considered by others too. The field of attention is narrowed. A new gestalt is created. The image of the analyst is introjected and incorporated into the patient's unconscious ego. This he feels accounts for the creation of a special form of rapport as a result of which rapid exploration of the unconscious can take place in hypnoanalysis. The additional inference that he makes is often questionable, I believe. He says the analyst loses the "chameleon" quality projected upon him as a result of the patient's resistances and defenses when in the waking state. The effect on the resistances appears, I believe, to be exaggerated. The therapeutic benefits derived are probably related to a more pervasive psychological reorientation within the hypnotic state, allowing for inner perceptions and realignments not necessarily connected with the interpersonal contact between doctor and patient. In other words, transference elements play a role, though not the only role in the induction of hypnosis. They can be utilized for therapeutic benefit in hypnotic interactions. They need not, however, account for everything that transpires.

The fallacy of attempting to account for hypnosis on the basis of transference exclusively is allied, I think, to the fallacy of linking it only to suggestion. The historical links with suggestion can be dated back to Braid and to Bernheim if only two examples are to be given, but there are other important names before them and since (Schneck, 12, 31, 32). Suggestion can play a role in helping to further therapeutic gains with it. But suggestion cannot account for all happenings within the hypnotic setting and this in turn is true for transference.

Writings on the nature and theory of hypnosis are numerous. Many are not of fundamental concern to investigators and practitioners of psychoanalytic hypnotherapy. It is neither possible nor pertinent to discuss at length the variety of concepts proposed, so I shall merely note a few references to writings of relatively recent years for those concerned. Then there will be taken up some views with a more concentrated psychoanalytic focus. The papers of related interest are by Arnold (33), Barber (34), Guze (35), Kline (36), Koster (37), Sarbin (38), Orne (56), Weitzenhoffer (57), White (58), and Solovey (59). Some of the themes they touch include the mechanism of suggestion, the psychology of belief and perception, hypnosis as emotional response, hypnotic retrogression, hypnosis and sleep, and role-taking theory.

In psychoanalytic writings, the role of transference is highlighted in attempts to formulate a meaningful understanding of the hypnotic state, or, as many of us are inclined to think of it today, hypnotic states—the variety of experiences covering a broad spectrum subsumed under the heading of such state or states. Unconscious, instinctual, infantile drives are given special attention. The theme of the hypnotic contact reflecting a reactivation of the oedipal relationship is encountered often. In line with this, Ferenczi (18) spoke of maternal and paternal forms of hypnosis. This view generally sees the first predicated on reactions of love, and the second on fear. I believe this is an oversimplification because the love-fear dichotomy does not necessarily exist and its ingredients are more complex. Even if the maternal-paternal notion were taken at face value, there are combinations present at times in any one case that make an attempt at differentiation rather artificial. Although the concept may have carried an impression of depth when Ferenczi first presented his views, the notion depicts a rather superficial level of operation that hardly serves to separate a view of the hypnotic contact from many other interpersonal relations having no connections with hypnotic procedure.

A view of Freud (17) has been alluded to already. It entails a connection between hypnosis and a love relationship,"... the same humble subjection, the same compliance, the same absence of criticism towards the hypnotist just as toward the loved object." The description appears to be an oversimplification of an hypnotic relationship where often enough one observes considerable criticism, conflict over compliance, defiance in lieu of humble subjection, all of which may nevertheless be utilized by the hypnoanalyst as a means of promoting the development of hypnotic reactions rather than serving as means to evade hypnotic response. Freud sees the hypnotist serving as an ego-ideal which I believe is so for many patients, perhaps with more complex implications than he surmised, as reflected in various clinical sections in this book. Furthermore, hypnosis is more than a group of two, as has been stressed in comments on his views, not only in terms of the multiplicity of identifications with only two participants, but with the additional complex identifications among members of a larger group, in group therapy for example. In addition his views as well as similar pronouncements by others do not explain hypnotic phenomena in lower forms of life among various animal species and so limit themselves to human involvements.

The libidinal elements in hypnotic interaction were alluded to by Schilder (20). Readers may be interested also in a recent view of his broader contributions to psychoanalytic psychiatry (55). I have had occasion in a number of writings to spell out in greater detail the presence of homosexual as well as heterosexual strivings among patients in hypnoanalysis, within the hypnotic relationship —strivings that Schilder also made reference to in connection with the hypnotic bond. The point about hysterical subjects being particularly susceptible to hypnosis in keeping with the tendency to fixate love objects strongly, is, however, a rather complex item. I dwell on it elsewhere in this volume when I stress the libidinal ties less than the individual's reaction to his own degree of suggestibility. In line with this, hysterical patients as well as others who tend to react against, or to resist the expression of their suggestibility propensities will have difficulties of one sort of another with hypnotic induction and the hypnotic setting. The issue is pertinent too even if one were to include the characteristic of suggestibility among libidinal features, to which I have no objection within the context of this theme as it is being discussed now.

Schilder deals, as do others too, with the interpersonal elements and transference features of hypnosis when, for example, he talks of patients realizing their infantile power, magic, and omnipotence fantasies through identification with the hypnotist whom they imbue with these attributes. The point is important in connection with the nature of hypnosis because again, the issue of self-hypnosis is introduced as a setting wherein a hypnotist seen in this way is not present at all. The counter-argument states at times that the hypnotist enveloped in a particular aura is fantasied in self-hypnosis. I suppose it may be an unconscious fantasy as well as a conscious fantasy. At times this may be so, but the claim can be stretched indefinitely. If not a real person, one can say that among some groups of people, perhaps primitives, the fantasy can involve a god or gods with their father-like characteristics or father or mother implications. Should this be done, the point of the father-hypnotist or some similar identification, with or without associated oedipal significance, can always be introduced. The theme becomes weak, however, when one considers the nature of hypnosis more pervasively by including sub-human forms of life.

In dealing with theoretical contributions to hypnosis, there was mentioned in at least one source (39) the views of Rado (40), although it is not clear why this was done if stress is to be placed on perceptions growing out of a wealth of clinical experience rather than impressions gained largely indirectly by application of standard psychoanalytic views to most any type of activity that can presumably be explained comfortably by such views. The idea that a transference neurosis is or can be set up in a hypnotic relationship is surely true, as it is in non-hypnotic psychoanalytic settings, but the idea that the transference remains unresolved is both questionable and generally untrue. In this assumption that it does remain unresolved when hypnosis is employed, the patient supposedly relives repeatedly the transference fantasy responsible for the cure. Now this may be so at times. Usually it is not. I should say it is frequently true in psychoanalytic treatment supposedly brought to a successful conclusion. This is often encountered today. It is my impression it is more true in non-hypnotic psychoanalytic situations than in hypnotherapeutic or hypno-analytic encounters.

In dealing with hypnosis some time ago, Kubie (41) stressed the different aspects of the hypnotic process and the hypnotic state. He recognized difficulties in defining hypnosis and said it is necessary, therefore, "to approximate the clarity of a definition by accurate description, by analogies where necessary, by an analysis of methods, and by measurements wherever possible." He spoke of limiting sensori-motor communication between subject and outside world during induction. As a result "the hypnotist becomes temporarily the sole representative of and contact with the outside world." Here ensues the patient-child hypnotist-subject analogy. Onset of the hypnotic state consists of "partial sleep." Ego boundaries are obliterated. There is a psychological fusion between hypnotist and subject. In this second phase, after limitation of sensori-motor communication with the outside, "the words of the hypnotist became indistinguishable from his own thoughts," and "it is this in turn which makes possible all of the phenomena of *apparent* passive suggestibility." I might mention parenthetically that these descriptions and allegations are surely in the experience of those with very extensive hypnotic encounters, applicable to a fraction only, and really a small fraction of subjects and patients. The spectrum of hypnotic experience is so much broader. It is worth noting that there is focus of attention on the sleep issue by Kubie, reminiscent of Pavlovian themes which had been quite influential in hypnosis research and which still are quite important in the activities of Russian and other European investigators at present.

Kubie and Margolin (41) went on to say in summarizing their views, "Physiologically the hypnotic process is shown to be an extension of the processes of normal attention, the result of the creation in the central nervous system of a concentrated focus of excitation with the surrounding areas of inhibition (in the descriptive Pavlovian sense)." In the final phase the hypnotic state involves, according to them, a partial re-expansion of ego boundaries and an incorporation of a fragmentary image of the hypnotist within the expanded boundaries of the subject's ego. This view appears to be predicated on acceptance of the description of the preceding phrases which, I think, may be an artifact. The suppression of outside stimuli and the limited sensori-motor intake is often helpful for the induction, but for some subjects who do not expect the necessity for this, the self-absorption peculiar to hypnotic experience does not necessarily require drastic limitation of sensori-motor contact with the outside. The contact is altered, but in a selective way, often spontaneously selective, and to a degree necessary for the individual subject or patient.

Then, the statement is made regarding the final phase of the hypnotic process according to the aforementioned conceptions, that it parallels the phase in the infant's developing ego where its boundaries expand with retention of parental images as unconscious incorporated components of the developing ego. Here, the incorporated image of the hypnotist has a role for the subject that the incorporated unconscious image of a parental figure has for a child or adult. "Hypnosis thus is seen to be an experimental reproduction of a natural developmental process." I believe it does include the aforementioned components but that in addition it possesses phylogenetic associations as will be mentioned later. It is of interest that when the paper from which these quotations and views are taken was published, a point was made in it to the effect that the use of hypnosis in some form may conceivably be necessary for effective displacement of retained, disturbing, superego figures. Kubie repeated a number of his opinions in a more recent publication (42).

It may be worth noting again that Kubie was interested in the physiological as well as the psychological components of the hypnotic process. This is more than a simple statement of fact, because in the development of psychoanalysis any such interest was at times, and by many considered somewhat suspect. It should be pointed out too in regard to the issue of hypnosis and sleep, that Freud saw in the stress on it an attempt fundamentally to focus the interest of the subject on the hypnotist and away from other concerns. Schilder, however, thought in terms of the sleep center of the third ventricle in his theorizing about hypnosis. Furthermore, the ideas of various egos in connection with this theme—sleep ego, dream ego, waking ego—is a reminder of what is being talked about today, namely a view of hypnosis as involving not a specifically circumscribed hypnotic state, but "states" or something akin to this, implying a more fluid concept, or, if you will, a concept of greater fluidity in that realm of consciousness with which we are concerned when speaking and thinking in terms of hypnosis.

In general, however, writings with psychoanalytic orientations continue to stress the theme of transference and the play of interpersonal issues in any attempt to theorize about hypnosis. In doing so, there is often reliance on views of others who have themselves had little or no practical experience in hypnosis areas so that the concepts put forward are essentially second hand. Not long ago, Spiegel (43), who is concerned with hypnosis issues, presented his views, and in prefacing his definition called on statements by others as I have just indicated. Rioch (44) was noted as having followed Horney's lead, and transference was pointed up as an interpersonal experience with the willingness to surrender emphasized as a crucial precursor for trance experience. Many hypnosis investigators would acknowledge its significance for certain subjects but would regard it, I believe, as far from crucial for others. Thompson (45), whose writings I think show in their few pertinent statements somewhat limited awareness of hypnotic transactions, is mentioned in connection with the view that analysis aims at resolving irrational attitudes, but the irrational attitudes may be used therapeutically without such resolution. I should agree with this. Finally, Silverberg (46) is referred to for the view that transference links irrational qualities with the repetition compulsion. Spiegel went on to outline his "working definition" of hypnosis and referred to it as an altered state of relatedness. It is characterized by an irrational submission and entails the abandonment of executive control as a regressed, dissociated state ensues, a state that is actively instigated and enhanced by the hypnotist. Spiegel says this is a transactional, descriptive statement of what may happen in hypnosis. He adds that there is another way of saying this. Trance induction and maintenance are pure transference experience. Trance induction is transference action. Trance maintenance is transference in a "frozen state." In a preliminary comment about hypnosis and transference he said that one of the points of confusion had to do with the effort to correlate data from hypnotic phenomena with the libido concept of transference. But he feels that the libido concept of transference "bogs down by its own weight" and that its usefulness as a frame of reference in clinical areas is limited. Again it must be pointed out that any view of hypnosis based on interpersonal elements, whether or not the issue of transference in its specific psychoanalytic connotations is stressed, limits understandings to certain aspects of human functioning and disregards basically the features of functioning in other living forms that have been studied in relation to all so-called hypnotic phenomena. If observations of other forms are to be excluded in theorizing about hypnosis, this must be done by definition, with all implied limitations. I doubt that it can be done if more is to be understood about hypnosis in its fundamentals, certainly about hypnosis as a biological issue rather than the more limited "psychological" aspects of biological operations.

Those who are inclined to fall back on views of hypnosis expressing essentially the fundamental themes of Freud, Ferenczi, and other psychoanalytic opinions of that era will find alleged substantiation in the contributions of Speyer and Stokvis (19). They obtained accounts of experiences in hypnosis when a man hypnotized a woman and a woman hypnotized a man, with findings that led them to be impressed by the libidinal components. They concluded that the erotic attitude of the hypnotized person toward the hypnotizer plays an important role in the establishment of an hypnotic state. Regressions take place in hypnosis that constitute reactivation of the oedipal situation. The castration complex is revived. Sadistic and masochistic features are revealed, and so on. While Brenman and Gill were inclined to say that psychoanalysts furnished the "most penetrating statements of interpersonal relationships between hypnotist and subject," they felt, for example, not long after the Speyer and Stokvis publication appeared, that psychoanalytic theories did not "define the specificity of the hypnotic state," noting that transference relationships exist also in non-hypnotic interpersonal contacts (39).

Just as hypnoanalytic and related developments have kept pace with growing dynamic concepts in psychiatry and psychoanalysis in general, so too have theoretical notions of hypnosis tended to be correlated with changing views of personality and psychoanalytic theory. Bellak (47), to give one illustration, spoke about an ego-psychological theory of hypnosis. He spoke of hypnosis as a special case of the self-excluding function of the ego. He said a topological regression occurs from conscious perception to preconscious functioning. It was similar to the performance of routine tasks where a small aspect of cognitive function persists. In hypnosis it is directed toward the hypnotist. He believed that various aspects of hypnosis could be understood and evaluated in terms of ego functioning, pointing the way of course to a greater integration of hypnotic functioning with ego psychology. Again, however, there is reluctance, as is evident too with others, to abandon libido concepts. Libidinal factors, he says, should not be ignored and a theory of hypnosis needs to include the libidinal relationship between hypnotist and patient. Bellak says that the hypnotic state which has so often been described as a state of narrowed consciousness, can be understood better as a state of partial self-exclusion of the ego. It is similar to falling asleep but not identical with it. He points out that it is necessary for the ego to be able to exclude itself and he refers also to the theme that has been touched on by others regarding a regression in the service of the ego, with special reference to Kris (48) as far as this particular theme is concerned.

If psychoanalytic theories of hypnosis with their repetitions and slight variations are not enough, is there anything that serves as a more attractive attempt to explain hypnosis, or at least to cover its characteristics and attributes more completely? At times mention is made of its atavistic features, but this point also is mentioned now and then in a specific way in psychoanalytic opinions. It is made elsewhere too. Meares (54) has centered attention on an atavistic theory of hypnosis, but the regressive features he mentions are essentially an extension of the theme of suggestion which reappears constantly in hypnosis literature including that on theory, stemming from earlier nineteenth century views. My own thinking has been along the lines of hypnosis as related to a fundamental core in all living things, and as such it turns to issues of evolution and a view of hypnosis as basic in phylogenetic developments. Actually, I did not stress this term in earlier writings although the ideas were there. I spoke only of a theory of hypnosis, or a psychophysiological view, and then more inclusively of a biological view (Schneck, 51-53). But the phylogenetic issue is involved. The term has appeared elsewhere. Guze (49), for example, spoke of the phylogeny of hypnosis, but the opinions he rendered appear to be more limited in scope than what I have proposed although I do not believe that what he had to say contradicts the ideas I presented. Guze, in his own words, made "an attempt to derive hypnosis phylogenetically from the basic adient-abient and emotional responsiveness of organisms." He thought of hypnosis functionally as a state of readiness for emotional action "increasingly subordinated to cortical influences as one ascends phylogeny, but nonetheless consistently present in animal organisms in a variety of forms."

Much has been written about animal hypnosis if one views the literature dating back well into the last century. Marcuse (50) has contributed to this field and I make reference in passing to only one of his publications, without entering into details of his views or those of additional investigators. They are removed from our special focus of attention here, but I stress the need to consider animal hypnosis, and I emphasize too a broad view of all forms of life in relation to concern about theory. I think psychoanalytic play on interpersonal and transference features touches on a limited aspect of the nature of hypnosis at its core.

I think a basic fallacy in most theories is the tendency to focus mainly on hypnotic induction and on phenomena elicited in the hypnotic setting. Presumably there is concern with the essence of the hypnotic experience, but usually it is not approached at all. For an approach to its basic ingredient it seems pertinent to concentrate on that condition most removed from ordinary waking experience and from sleep states as we know them. The basic condition may be aimed at self-hypnotically or heterohypnotically. Theoretically, the basic aspect of hypnosis is approached in its most pure form when the usual thinking processes associated with conscious awareness are altered to a degree that contact with the environment is markedly reduced and the hypnotic subject experiences the minimum of self-awareness of which we can conceive, and, as a corollary, the minimum degree of differentiation of his "self" from the "environment" in so far as this is possible. At the core of hypnosis, for humans, the extent of dissipation of environmental contact would be greater than, at the very least, the absence of awareness of time, place, and person. When this condition is attained, the individual has moved in the direction of functioning approaching the most primitive level of psychophysiological operations of living organisms where the very first note of awareness of individual-environmental differentiation occurs. I suspect, in this phylogenetic theory, that this basic psychophysiological differentiation of individual and environment is the essence of the hypnotic state, and as such is the core or basic state that we have of late come to label hypnosis.

Much evidence has been put forward regarding complex psychological, sociological, and physiological aspects of hypnosis. The validity of evidence along these lines is not refuted by the phylogenetic theory of hypnosis. The basic state I refer to entails a profound regression, and various living forms can regress only just so far, the degree varying with their fundamental biological capacities, and in the case of humans with their capacities that vary considerably as individuals. The direction of the regression in all living forms is, however, in this basic direction. The psychological (and psychoanalytic specifically), sociological, and physiological aspects of the hypnotic setting are secondary features important in themselves, but not primary indicators of the nature of hypnosis. Many of these features appear in non-hypnotic situations. Some appear more prominently as a result of measures taken to help induce changes in the patient or subject that move him in the direction of the regression I have proposed. The types and degrees of regression vary considerably both quantitatively and qualitatively, and from this emerges the notion of hypnotic "states" that we hear more about now. These are indeed variants of organizational components of personality within the fundamental direction of the regression.

Various theories that have been proposed appear to relate more to the operational and phenomenological aspects of induction or behavior during various levels of psychophysiological changes that are reached along the continuum from the ordinary waking state or the sleep state to the hypnotic state in its most simple, basic, or primitive form. During the course of whatever functional alterations come about as part of this regression in the individual as he moves to various "levels" of hypnosis, complex forms of functioning ensue spontaneously or may be induced heterohypnotically. In psychoanalytic terms, these go hand in hand with varying degrees of narrowing and expanding of ego boundaries during the course of the regression. But in a psychoanalytic setting and in the psychoanalytic framework, the regression is a tiny fragment, a small feature of human capacity, of the more global phylogenetic regression encompassing all life forms. Transference and other interpersonal issues are minor parts of, or expressions of the regression. They reflect in humans certain aspects of the regression. Interpersonal relations may foster or reflect regression. They do not define hypnosis.

The phylogenetic theory implies that the primitive condition, the core of hypnosis, would actually constitute a state somewhere between organic and inorganic existence. It would be a primordial state serving as a substratum for later development of more complex life experience. Regression, in terms of a reversal of the developmental continuum, would transcend chronological age-year regression and would incorporate ontogenetic and phylogenetic regression. Various other theories have common denominators and overlap. Often they appear to contradict one another. I think all of them, to the degree to which they are meaningfully explanatory of aspects of hypnotic experience, are encompassed by the phylogenetic view. It is more holistic than the others. The ideas expressed here, if carried to an obvious conclusion, imply that the hypnotic core is fundamentally related to the core of experience in what we discuss today as consciousness, and that this core may turn out to be fundamental to an understanding of states of waking and of sleep, and states of being and behavior that we categorize as normal and abnormal, the latter involving various expressions of functioning that we classify as illness. Occasionally we encounter now discussions of states of illness as involving similarities to, if not reflections of certain aspects of hypnotic experience. The hypnotic core appears to be related to the fundamentals of life processes. Its ingredients may be clarified in the future as a result of contributions from the field of a more broadly based biology rather than from its delimited segment, psychology.

8. Abreaction, Insight, and Related Concerns in Psychoanalytic Hypnotherapy

Early stages in the development of psychoanalysis entailed attention to the apparent importance of affect charged experiences which had been repressed and were later reactivated in the course of treatment. In time, the importance of such events and their abreaction was reevaluated and they began to play a lesser role in the over-all treatment situation and in the stress placed on them in terms of therapeutic value. Abreaction was significant too in the early phase of concern with hypnotherapy especially, although not necessarily in its link with psychoanalysis. Concentration of attention on abreactive methods may perhaps have continued longer in connection with hypnotic techniques than with other psychotherapeutic measures. In routine civilian practice, concerns with abreaction need not be as great when compared with the more unusual, highly traumatic wartime experiences. The link between abreaction and hypnotherapy may tend to be cemented for some because of the special association of effective hypnotherapy with highly charged wartime events. It would be incorrect to view abreaction as the fundamental issue in hypnotherapy and, on the basis of what has already been discussed, it should be evident that many complex theoretical and technical factors removed from the classic concepts of abreaction are of fundamental importance in hypnoanalysis as it is unfolding and developing now. Nevertheless, certain circumstances and treatment situations do entail a basic role for abreactions that are indeed significant in the relief of illness. The most dramatic often continue to involve wartime settings (Schneck, 24). The management of treatment and evaluations of its facets may rely heavily, however, on fundamental psychoanalytic concepts (Schneck, 12).

A twenty-one year old airman entered treatment because of recurrent, severe precordial pain. A crucial phase in his short-term contact entailed a highly dramatic and emotionally intense revivification of a combat mission during which his friend was killed when shot through the heart. Further exploration in his hypnotherapy involved his developmental years and his relationship with this friend and the latter's wife. Some of the main features, in working out the problem, were seen to relate to his unconscious identification with his friend, involvements with him and the wife beyond his conscious awareness, a reactivation of the oedipal situation in the interplay among them, attendant feelings of guilt, and finally a reassessment of the total situation with integration of present and past attitudes. It was felt at the time this patient was seen that identification with the therapist in the hypnotic situation may have enhanced the patient's ego strength as a result of which he could more easily accept consciously the previously highly cathected, repressed memories. I believe the identification with the fantasied strength of the hypnotherapist is often significant in treatment, but it must be assessed realistically in this respect. It does not argue for a negative view of hypnotic settings based on the erroneous belief of limited value and limited persistence of improvement. It may be the beginning of a phase of continued growth for the patient. Also, this identification occurs in non-hypnotic therapies, including traditional psychoanalysis, despite the reluctance of many to accept its importance in these areas of treatment.

Fantasies of patients about the strength of the hypnotherapist and the role of such fantasies in the attempt to augment ego strength are quite frequent in my opinion. Their basic elements probably differ little when compared with non-hypnotic therapies, but in the interpersonal relationship involving hypnosis there is evidently an intensification of these features. As a result, when improvement ensues in short-term contacts it is perhaps more easily achieved with hypnotherapy (Schneck, 25).

As part of the process of therapeutic change, I am inclined to think that the healthy reorganization of personality functioning in these instances involves significant unconscious alterations without the apparent necessity for full conscious appreciation of such alterations. The need for conscious understandings may be greater for patient and therapist alike in other treatment procedures. Actually, these conscious understandings may be more prone to lessen the anxiety of therapists than to prove vitally meaningful for beneficial changes in patients. Needless to say there are numerous exceptions. These issues are mentioned now because they applied to military service material just discussed. It may be added that there have been opportunities for many brief psychotherapy or first aid attempts involving hypnotherapy. In such treatment the hypnotic measures used are often specialized techniques and the theoretical background for clinical judgment is psychoanalytically anchored. The types of problems fitting this scheme vary somewhat. In military service they involve amnesic episodes not infrequently. One example concerned a young man who was partially amnesic for a homosexual experience the recall of which was linked to his need to evaluate related issues of crucial importance to him at that particular time. These issues were not consciously appreciated by him in their importance at that point. They included his sexual contact with an older woman who had also been similarly involved with the patient's father. Also, these matters related to his current interest in a young woman whose traits were linked with oedipal associations. Finally, the several ramifications touched on decisions with which the patient was faced in relation to a contemplated change of religious faith.

Interest in hypnoanalysis is not limited to possibilities for developing hypnotic methods advantageously for beneficial gain. It offers opportunities for greater insights into the meaning of the many facets of hypnosis and opportunities for augmenting knowledge about personality functioning in general. It was possible, in connection with treatment of a patient who had entered a fugue state with subsequent amnesia, to elucidate some aspects of the psychopathology of time control (Schneck, 12). The surface aspects of the problem involved conflict with a friend and an employer. There was considerable indecision regarding a certain course of action, and the pertinent issues were repressed. A fugue state that ensued was, for their patient, a period of problem solving. When he reached a decision the fugue state terminated and the entire constellation of events and related concerns was repressed with an amnesia covering the period of fugue. The patient proceeded to act on his decision as if the obliterated time period did not in fact exist at all. In a peculiar fashion for a case such as this, the patient functions as if he has gained control over time itself. The amnesia eliminated, in this case, the nature of the patient's problem, related conflicts, and associated feelings of guilt. More specifically in this instance there was a problem of sibling rivalry represented in the patient's contact with his friend, and its involvement of a father surrogate in the employer. Hypnotic methods were capable of removing the amnesia, clarifying the surface happenings during the fugue, and elucidating the underlying psychological issues, enabling the patient to gain some understanding of his mental functioning and behavioral tendencies.

References

1. Schneck, J. M.: Critical evaluation of hypnosis, in Wortis, S. B.: *Psychiatric Treatment*. Baltimore, Williams and Wilkins, 1953.

2. Schneck, J. M., and Kline, M. V.: A control study relating to H-T-P testing and hypnosis. *Brit. J. Med. Hyp., 3:2*, 1951.

3. Schneck, J. M., and Kline, M. V.: The H-T-P and TAT in hypno-diagnostic studies. *Brit. J. Med. Hyp., 5:3*, 1953.

4. Kent, G. H., and Rosanoff, A. J.: *Manual of Psychiatry*. New York, Wiley, 1938.

5. Kohs, S. C.: The association method in its relation to the complex and complex indicators. *Amer. J. Psychol., 25:*544, 1914.

6. Rapaport, D.: *Diagnostic Psychological Testing*. Chicago, Year Book Publishers, 1946, vol. 2.

7. Kline, M. V., and Schneck, J. M.: Hypnosis in relation to the Word Association Test. *J. Gen. Psychol., 44:*129, 1951.

8. Schneck, J. M.: Symptom relief, authority substitution, and suggestibility, with special reference to hypnotherapy. *Dis. Nerv. Syst., 20:*583, 1959.

9. Alexander, F.: Discussion of Hoch, P. H.: Aims and Limitations of Psychotherapy. *Amer. J. Psychiat., 112:*321, 1955.

10. Seitz, P. F. D.: Experiments in the substitution of symptoms by hypnosis. *Psychosom. Med., 15:*405, 1953.

11. Moll, A.: *Hypnotism*. London, Walter Scott, 1890.

12. Schneck, J. M.: *Studies in Scientific Hypnosis*. Baltimore, Williams and Wilkins, 1954.

13. Schneck, J. M.: The elucidation of spontaneous sensory and motor phenomena during hypnoanalysis. *Psychoanal. Rev., 39:*79, 1952.

14. Schneck, J. M.: Some aspects of homosexuality in relation to hypnosis. *Psychoanal. Rev., 37:*351, 1950.

15. Schneck, J. M.: Psychogenic gastrointestinal disorder and cephalalgia with paradoxical reactions to hypnosis. *J. Nerv. Ment. Dis., 117:*130, 1953.

16. Brenman, M., Gill, M. M., and Hacker, F. J.: Alterations in the state of the ego in hypnosis. *Bull. Menninger Clin., 11:*60, 1947.

17. Freud, S.: *Group Psychology and the Analysis of the Ego*, translated by James Strachey. New York, Boni and Liveright, 1924.

18. Ferenczi, S.: Introjection and transference, in *Contributions to Psychoanalysis*, translated by Ernest Jones. Boston, Richard G. Badger, 1916.

19. Speyer, N., and Stokvis, B.: The psycho-analytical factor in hypnosis. *Brit. J. M. Psychol., 17:*217, 1938.

20. Schilder, P., and Kauders, O. *Hypnosis*. New York, Nervous and Mental Disease Publishing Company, 1927.

21. Schneck, J. M.: The hypnoanalysis of phobic reactions, in Le Cron, L. M.: *Experimental Hypnosis*. New York, Macmillan, 1952.

22. Schneck, J. M.: Hypnotherapy of a patient with an animal phobia. *J. Nerv. Ment. Dis., 116:*48, 1952.

23. Schneck, J. M.: Hypnotic investigation and relief of recurrent anxiety episodes. *Dis. Nerv. Syst., 13:*142, 1952.

24. Schneck, J. M.: Psychogenic cardiovascular reaction interpreted and successfully treated with hypnosis. *Psychoanal. Rev., 35:*14, 1948.

25. Schneck, J. M.: Hypotherapeutic first-aid in military service. *Dis. Nerv. Syst., 14:*47, 1953.

26. Schneck, J. M., Ed.: *Hypnotherapy*. New York, Grune and Stratton, 1951.

27. Rush, B.: *Medical Inquiries and Observations upon the Diseases of the Mind* (1812), 5th Edition. Philadelphia, Grigg and Eliott, 1835.

28. Schneck, J. M.: Benjamin Rush on the influence of buried memories. *Dis. Nerv. Syst., 24:*173, 1963.

29. Schneck, J. M.: Transference and hypnotic behavior. *J. Clin. Exp. Hyp., 3:*132, 1955.

30. Lindner, R. M.: Hypnoanalysis as a psychotherapeutic technique, in *Specialized Techniques in Psychotherapy*. New York, Basic Books, 1953.

31. Schneck, J. M.: *Hypnosis in Modern Medicine*, 3rd Edition. Springfield, Ill., Thomas, 1963.

32. Schneck, J. M.: *A History of Psychiatry*. Springfield, Ill., Thomas, 1960.

33. Arnold, M. B.: On the mechanism of suggestion and hypnosis. *J. Abnorm. Soc. Psychol., 41:*107, 1946.

34. Barber, T. X.: The concept of "hypnosis." *J. Psychol., 45:*115, 1958.

35. Guze, H.: Hypnosis as emotional response: a theoretical approach. *J. Psychol., 35:*313, 1953.

36. Kline, M. V.: Hypnotic retrogression: a neuropsychological theory of age regression and progression. *J. Clin. Exp. Hyp., 1:*21, 1953.

37. Koster, S.: Experimental investigation of the character of hypnosis. *J. Clin. Exp. Hyp., 2:*42, 1954.

38. Sarbin, T. R.: Contributions to role-taking theory. 1. Hypnotic behavior. *Psychol. Rev., 57:*255, 1950.

39. Brenman, M., and Gill, M. M.: *Hypnotherapy*. Josiah Macy, Jr. Foundation, Review Series, 1944, Vol. 2, No. 3.

40. Rado, S.: The economic principle in psychoanalytic technique. *Int. J. Psychoanal.*, *6:*35, 1935.

41. Kubie, L. S., and Margolin, S.: The process of hypnotism and the nature of the hypnotic state. *Amer. J. Psychiat.*, *100:*611, 1944.

42. Kubie, L. S.: Hypnotism, a focus for psychophysiological and psycho-analytic investigations. *Arch. Gen. Psychiat.*, *4:*40, 1961.

43. Spiegel, H.: Hypnosis and transference, a theoretical formulation. *A.M.A. Arch. Gen. Psychiat.*, *1:*634, 1959.

44. Rioch, J. M.: The transference phenomenon in psychoanalytic therapy. *Psychiatry*, *6:*147, 1943.

45. Thompson, C.: Transference as a therapeutic instrument. *Psychiatry*, *8:*273, 1945.

46. Silverberg, W. V.: The concept of transference. *Psychoanal. Quart.*, *17:* 303, 1948.

47. Bellak, L.: An ego-psychological theory of hypnosis. *Int. J. Psycho-Anal.*, *36,*part 6, 1955.

48. Kris, E.: *Psychoanalytic Explorations in Art.* New York, International Universities Press, 1952.

49. Guze, H.: The phylogeny of hypnosis. *J. Clin. Exp. Hyp.*, *1:*41, 1953.

50. Marcuse, F. L.: Interpretation in animal hypnosis, in Schneck, J. M.: *Hypnosis and Personality.* New York, Grune and Stratton, 1951.

51. Schneck, J. M.: A theory of hypnosis. *J. Clin. Exp. Hyp.*, *1:*16, 1953.

52. Schneck, J. M.: Comment on a theory of hypnosis. *Int. J. Clin. Exp. Hyp.*, *8:231*, 1960.

53. Schneck, J. M.: Discussion of an atavistic theory of hypnosis, in Kline, M. V.: *The Nature of Hypnosis* (Transactions of the 1961 International Congress on Hypnosis). New York, Institute for Research in Hypnosis, 1961.

54. Meares, A.: A working hypothesis as to the nature of hypnosis. *A.M.A. Arch. Neurol. Psychiat.*, *77:*549, 1957.

55. Kaufman, M. R.: Schilder's application of psychoanalytic psychiatry. *Arch. Gen. Psychiat.*, *7:*311, 1962.

56. Orne, M. T.: The nature of hypnosis: artifact and essence. *J. Abnorm. Soc. Psychol.*, *58:*277, 1959.

57. Weitzenhoffer, A.: *Hypnotism.* New York, Wiley, 1953.

58. White, R. W.: A preface to a theory of hypnotism. *J. Abnorm. Soc. Psychol.*, *36:*477, 1941.

59. Solovey de Milechnin, G.: Concerning a theory of hypnosis. *J. Clin. Exp. Hyp.*, *4:*37, 1956.
60. Schneck, J. M.: Hypnotic phenomena apparently related to bilaterality. *J. Genet. Psychol.*, *80:*253, 1952.
61. Ames, L. B.: Bilaterality. *J. Genet. Psychol.*, *75:*45, 1949.
62. Gill, M. M.: Spontaneous regression on the induction of hypnosis. *Bull. Menninger Clin.*, *12:*41, 1948.
63. Gill, M. M., and Brenman, M.: *Hypnosis and Related States.* New York, International Press, 1959.

∽Part Three∽∽∽∽∽∽∽∽∽∽∽∽∽∽∽∽∽∽∽∽

1. Hypnoanalysis and Productiveness

THE HYPNOANALYTIC setting possesses great potential for productiveness in thinking, self-evaluation, and personality growth. Any lack of appreciation of such possibilities stems to some extent from inadequate insight into the potential richness of hypnotic behavior in a variety of settings. The main concept impeding acquisition of greater awareness is that of the hypnotic subject functioning essentially as an automaton (Schneck, 1). I believe a good illustration of this erroneous view may be found in a work by Fromm (2). Here, the activity of a subject under hypnosis is described as an extreme form of non-productivity. Although the hypnotized person is engaged in a variety of actions, he is regarded as not even the actor. It is the hypnotist who is the actor rather than the subject. The hypnotist acts through his subject by way of various suggestions. The activity of the subject is said to result from strong forces which he cannot control.

The belief just outlined, although fallacious, is widespread. It arises largely from impressions of hypnotic settings in entertainment areas where an aura of helplessness of the subject is fostered by the hypnotist. The abandonment of ego controls is more apparent than real in this particular relationship. Indeed, it is the subject-participant who brings into this exhibition complex needs which he finds satisfied by using the hypnotist for his purposes in this performance. The fine points will not be stressed here. Suffice it to say that hypnoanalytic efforts cannot be understood unless it is first recognized that a fluid, dynamic utilization by the patient of ego capacities is brought into play and manipulated basically by him, under guidance, in an effort to fathom, unravel, and constructively reorganize the most fruitful and adaptable elements in his personality structure and functioning. Patients who can employ hypnotic methods satisfactorily and who possess flexibility, adaptability, and productive potential are the subjects who can achieve most in hypnoanalysis. They may possibly do well with more traditional psychoanalytic approaches, but they can often transcend such progress if the several hypnotic techniques in hypnoanalytic work serve them well.

2. Exhibitionism and Deception

In uncontrolled demonstration settings, hypnotic subjects often find expression for exhibitionistic and sado-masochistic needs. The setting, the audience, and the hypnotist are used for this purpose. Such needs, were they to be introduced into an hypnotic setting when a hypnoanalysis is initiated, are to be recognized by the hypnoanalyst who is then in a position to accept them initially for leverage, and eventually to analyze them with the patient as participant. What the hypnosis can do here is to highlight the pathological strivings and display, to sharpen the focus, to demonstrate more clearly than ever the attributes and the underlying mechanisms of the sick personality. Often the hypnotic setting and relationship, indeed the induction phase itself, brings to the fore in bold relief the chief elements in personality operation, elements otherwise more diffuse and recognized with greater difficulty. One must consider too that patients seeking and entering hypnoanalysis are influenced by entertainment hypnosis seen by them or about which they have been told. Routine but widespread misconceptions are acquired or reenforced. Unfortunately these erroneous ideas influence the approach to induction and also affect certain understandings in treatment. Fortunately it is possible at times to link misconceptions with fantasies about hypnosis. In so doing the potential detriments may be converted into meaningful therapeutic gains when assisting patients in fathoming the significance of their fantasies relating specifically to hypnosis at first, but carrying broader personality implications as they are evaluated further. The direct and indirect contact of patients with popular exhibitions of hypnosis affect expectations, hypnotic behavior, interpretations, and transference relationships.

Regarding entertainment hypnosis, I have been able to point up certain subtleties in hypnotist-subject and hypnotist-audience relationships with subject-audience identifications through co-entertainer status (Schneck, 3). Of primary interest in hypnoanalysis as an extension of this theme, are the patient-hypnoanalyst identifications incorporating transference and countertransference phenomena. Some of the transference and countertransference issues in hypnoanalysis are similar to those in routine psychoanalytic methods, others are intensifications of such issues, while still others involve special features based on the hypnotic facets specifically. The complex relationships, some of which are of interest in connection with the interpersonal features of hypnosis entertainment, are not especially connected with other interesting points having to do with intentional deceptions in some hypnotist-subject-audience settings. This has been evaluated by hypnosis investigators such as Wells (4).

Some patients seeking hypnoanalysis express mild interest in the issue of deception as far as stage demonstrations are concerned. As an extension of such interest they may inquire about the possibility of self-injurious behavior and asocial or anti-social acts relating to hypnotic functioning. Serious inquiry because of personal concern usually raises the question of paranoid content. This in turn should be explored further owing to hesitancies in proceeding with hypnoanalytic work in private practice or clinics, and institutional out-patient settings, when paranoid elements are significant in patients' difficulties. When such problems are not involved, patients occasionally express interest in the use of hypnosis for anti-social intentions as part of an over-all curiosity about the subject in general. There is little need to stress reassurance on this score because patients with reasonably intact ego structures accept, without question, the ethical professional atmosphere as one wherein misuse of hypnotic methods need not be considered any more than one would question the good intentions of physicians in any other area of practice.

I encountered a minor but nonetheless interesting example of a breech of military regulations by a patient when circumstances were such that its likely occurrence could not have been foretold in advance by the therapist himself. It was important for the study of hypnosis because a clinical rather than experimental setting was involved (Schneck, 5). There are many complex issues that enter into the utilization of hypnosis for anti-social purposes. They include the nature of the clinical or experimental setting, personality of the subject, hypnotic methods employed, perceptual distortions possible through hypnotic manipulations, personality of the hypnotist (actual, and fantasied by the subject) and the fine points in the interpersonal relationship between hypnotist and subject. Other factors are involved and they are of concern not only in connection with the basic issue of inducing anti-social behavior, but in my opinion as illustrations of much broader aspects of personality functioning regardless of obvious concerns relating to malevolent intent, subject response, and ethical considerations.

The clinical setting for the case mentioned above involved treatment of a patient for a brief period of amnesia. The use of hypnosis, aside from dispelling the amnesia, was connected with the arrangements for a subsequent treatment contact at a time evidently satisfactory for patient and doctor. Subsequent events, unforeseen by either, made the appointment time inadvisable, but the patient followed through in accordance with prior arrangements, and as a result brought on an infraction of military regulations. The clinical aspect of the problem highlighted its significance at the time. Experimental explorations of the problem of anti-social and self-injurious behavior have interested many investigators including Bramwell (6), Rowland (7), Wells (7), and Young (9). Estabrooks (10) reviewed some of the literature and Reiter (11) produced a book containing an extensive account of a case that attracted considerable attention.

Aside from the interest of some patients in questions of deception and anti-social behavior produced or influenced by hypnosis, medico-legal issues may occasionally come to light in hypno-analytic settings. In recent years they have not had special significance, and whatever importance they may have played would have been consistent essentially with such issues as part of psychiatric practice in general. With future expansion of the use of hypnoanalysis this picture may change and these problems may merit more attention. The special feature, as far as hypnoanalysis is concerned, is the role of hypnotic technique and phenomena in influencing the features of the medico-legal concerns. I encountered this problem some time ago during the hypnoanalysis of a member of a prison population under military jurisdiction. An attempt was made by some prisoners to obtain firearms and an escape was effected. The patient knew the whereabouts of these men. During the course of an hypnotic session he revealed this information. He was capable of achieving complete posthypnotic amnesias spontaneously and on suggestion. He would also develop partial amnesias spontaneously and selectively in accordance with the psychodynamic significance of the interview contents. This is just what he did in connection with these revelations. The occurrence was managed therapeutically by a series of comments and questions put to him which eventually permitted him to realize consciously what he had said. Although a special military prison setting was involved here, its counterparts in routine civilian practice should be clear.

The dynamics are of interest. The patient could not share his knowledge freely with his doctor because of an identification with fellow prisoners. The guilt engendered would have been too great. Yet he identified himself also with the therapist and would have felt guilty about withholding this knowledge. By virtue of his intelligence and social background too, he felt different from the other men. The ability to achieve selective spontaneous amnesias permitted him to withhold information on a waking level, yet to reveal it in hypnosis, covering up any conscious awareness of what he had done. Allegiance to the prisoners and to the therapist could be maintained, and guilt resolved. Yet the revelation may have involved a hostile component in that he could offer it to an individual who was in part representative of authority. It may have been a subtle, contemptuous gesture. Perhaps more important than these factual and conjectured details is the implication of this happening for the peculiarly complex and fine points inherent in certain aspects of hypnosis behavior.

3. Hypnoanalysis and the Hypnosis-death Concept

Hypnoanalysis has offered further opportunities for illustrating the complex elements involved in the significance and utilization of the hypnotic state. I was able to uncover the interesting fact that some people unconsciously equate the hypnotic state with death. This equating does not imply an "as if" relationship. Sometimes the feeling is so sudden and overwhelming that the patient experiences a strong need to reject it. This need is not, however, experienced by all patients and their way of coping with the awareness varies in accordance with their personality requirements. The equating of hypnosis and death may apply to the state induced heterohypnotically and autohypnotically too. On theoretical grounds the identification is of interest in connection with the idea of a death instinct. Although I have offered some pertinent allusions to it, the theme can probably be developed further (Schneck, 13). There are links also to observations on animal hypnosis with particular reference to the theme of death feigning in some animal forms. I have reason to believe that the issue of hypnosis and death is pertinent to a view of total psychobiological functioning. It is curious that this observation, while an outgrowth of hypnoanalytic practice, may indeed offer an important connection between certain aspects of human hypnosis and animal hypnosis (14). The equating of hypnosis and death came as a surprise to me as it emerged from clinical hypnoanlytic experience, but I was interested in finding, as is often the case in other aspects of psychoanlytic work, that the theme had already been in evidence in some literary works. Two pertinent examples that may be consulted further are the writings of Poe (15) and Du Maurier (16).

It has been suggested that the equating of hypnosis with death as an element in psychobiological functioning may imply a protective device in the form of a defense reaction to individual-environmental conflict and to intrapsychic conflict also. The hypnosis-death concept need not exist in isolation and, as a matter of fact, often merges with other psychodynamic issues, some of which may be linked to well known transference concerns. For example, a young man had a dream about a woman lying on a cot, dead. His associations pointed to the cot being identified with the office couch, with the woman representing the patient. Furthermore, the patient, in hypnosis, was identified with the woman and the hypnotic state was death. The patient felt himself to be passive and feminine in hypnosis. The hypnoanalyst was identified with the patient's father. The patient's interest in the use of hypnosis permitted him to place responsibility on the therapist for failure of treatment, as a means of expressing his hostile feelings. Analysis also revealed that the hypnotic relationship represented a homosexual contact. The connection between hypnosis and death may be made as a conscious association with an "as if" or resemblance implication. Yet for some, an "it is the same" relationship seems to exist and the equating takes place on an unconscious level. The identification, as indicated, merges with other concurrent psychodynamic themes (Schneck, 17).

4. Visual Imagery and Hallucinations in Hypnoanalysis

The "as if" association may be related to certain types of hallucinatory experiences described by some patients. The feeling that an extremity is absent or that it is present without sensation is encountered often. At times patients may describe absence of feeling in the entire body and this may suggest the theme of death. But this is to be differentiated from the central concept just outlined.

A variety of kinesthetic hallucinations were implied in the discussion of sensory and motor phenomena occurring spontaneously. Spontaneous visual and auditory hallucinations appear less frequently in hypnoanalysis. By visual hallucination I have in mind the state of the subject in which his eyes are open at the time. The auditory hallucinations are more frequent than the visual. Spontaneous positive and negative hallucinations, that take place in an apparent attempt to solve conflicts, have been described in relation to laboratory experimental situations by Lundholm (18). The frequency with which spontaneous hallucinations occur in treatment settings is difficult to evaluate accurately, because as in the case of various spontaneous sensory phenomena, their presence is not revealed regularly by patients. They are discovered at times when patients respond to questions about them. In this connection I am not taking into consideration states of regression and revivification and work with psychotic patients. It is, of course, the function of hypnoanalytic efforts to fathom the significance of such hallucinatory episodes whenever possible (Schneck, 19).

During her hypnoanalysis, a young woman felt on one occasion that a third person was in the room. The patient heard her conversing with the doctor but the content of their comments was not clear. Since this type of experience was unique for her and she was concerned about its possible pathological implications, the patient did not mention the episode until later in treatment. She identified the hallucinated voice as that of her mother. When this happening was explored hypnoanalytically, specific findings emerged. She was, at the time of the incident, identifying her mother with the hypnoanalyst. Finding this objectionable, the fused images became separated. That of her mother was not reintrojected, resulting in its representation as an external stimulus. Her feelings of hostility toward her mother were projected onto the hallucinated image. They were then experienced by the patient in the form of critical comment. In the auditory hallucination, her mother and her doctor were seen to be engaged in a critical conversation about her. Here again we have evidence in hypnoanalytic settings of peculiar alterations in ego functioning with special qualities that permit meaningful and helpful analysis. Needless to say, patients must retain sufficient ego strength and integration to take advantage of such opportunities. The nature of such occurrences when viewed out of context may imply more severe impairment in personality functioning than is actually the case. In fact, seemingly pathological experiences as illustrations of special hypnotic behavior occur often in people who may be quite well integrated in their over-all personality operations.

In connection with visual hallucinations, I believe it is important to differentiate between imagery observed by the subject when his eyes are closed, and images perceived when eyes are open. I prefer to avoid the term "hallucination" in relation to the first phenomenon which is, in fact, encountered frequently both clinically and experimentally. The hypnotic state appears to enhance abilities to experience visual imagery and to utilize it constructively. Some people can utilize such imagery under certain circumstances without a trance state. Some types of daydreaming offer pertinent examples of this. To refer to such functioning as hallucinatory seems to deprive the term of the significance usually associated with it.

The fact that hypnotic imagery may sometimes assume unique qualities is illustrated in a patient who described happenings that fall into the pattern of a spontaneous left homonymous hemianopsia within the context of such imagery. I had occasion to describe this is greater detail (Schneck, 20). The bisected field contained, at various times, views of the skeleton of her deceased husband, an image of her sister with carnival-like distortions, and impressions of herself in an agitated state. She was aware of straining to see what lay behind the blacked out portion of her field of vision. The representation of part of herself, closed to view, apparently reflected her conflict over latent homosexual tendencies manifesting themselves at this time also in other ways. Part of this conflict involved certain aspects of her relationships with her husband and sister. Although the patient's experience in hypnosis was rather individualistic, the occurrence has broader connections with psychogenic visual disturbances that I have reported elsewhere (Schneck, 21) and with comments by Dunbar (22), Fenichel (23), and Freud (24).

Of the visual disturbances among patients in my own clinical experience, one example is that of a patient who noted a film or veil encompassing her field of vision. She had entered treatment for a neurotic depression. The veil was revealed to be a psychological representation of a barrier that she felt was separating her from other people and the world about her. It was consistent with her feeling apart from others, often detached. The veil lifted as she evaluated her problems and established more meaningful personal relationships. Another patient noticed a blurring of vision when he focussed on certain objects. Study in this case showed that this occasional, selective blurring was, in its distortions, a psychological representation of his striving with difficulty to see himself in new perspectives. Its periodic intensification paralleled his attempt to deal with personality distortion and to effect remolding. Episodes of blurring diminished with the trend toward desirable personality change.

It would be a mistake to expect visual imagery in hypnosis to be constantly dramatic. As a matter of fact, there is usually an absence of the dramatic in any given series of hypnoanalytic sessions when isolated abreactions are excluded. The real importance of imagery, after all, is the representation of significant material from a psychodynamic point of view and in a way that permits the development of greater understandings and eventual preparation for change. During one of her hypnoanalytic sessions a twenty-eight year old married woman became increasingly involved in a discussion of her sexual concerns. Her activities were promiscuous and generally lacking in feeling. She was able to reveal that she would see the male sexual organ as an object of interest to her, divorced from any association with the man of whom it was a part. She viewed it as an impersonal object. She would focus on its "pumping and grinding" action and on her grasping it as a possession of her own. It denoted a masturbatory object for her. At the conclusion of the hypnosis, she commented on the light feeling of her arms and their folded position on her body. This reminded her of the "layed out dead body." She was concerned with the non-feeling elements in her sexual contacts.

5. Hypnotic Contradiction of Waking Verbalizations, and Enhanced Verbalization

The patient mentioned above illustrated also another occurrence quite common in hypnoanalysis. Claims made casually and honestly during the non-hypnotic phase of some sessions may be immediately contradicted by statements that follow during hypnosis, without the use of special techniques or probing attempts. For example, she mentioned one day that she had been feeling uneasy and depressed without real evidence of progress in treatment. During the hypnosis she mentioned spontaneously that she had evidently experienced the need to say this but in fact she had been feeling better and saw indications of healthy personality changes slowly emerging. This type of occurrence is encountered in a rather casual atmosphere quite often. Needless to say, on occasions and with other patients the statements may be reversed. A patient may allege experiencing meaningful improvements and proceed to discount this during hypnosis sessions, offering good reasons in support of the contradiction. The implications of such happenings will vary among patients and for the same patient at different times.

Once in a while the setting may be far different from the casual atmosphere just referred to. A woman in her thirties tended often to reveal considerable affect in hypnosis sessions. She would frequently state that she was feeling quite well and composed, without pressing problems. Soon after induction, the composure would give way to highly emotional behavior and evidence refuting earlier statements. The induction of hypnosis apparently has this influence often on the forces of repression. In more subtle ways, with ceratin patients, the barrier of isolation is clearly revealed and penetrated in the hypnotic setting.

It is simply a statement of fact that some people in hypnosis are capable of verbalizing certain points which in non-hypnotic sessions they are less inclined or able to offer as readily. In time they may be able to achieve this in routine interviews during free association or in conversational exchange. For them, the tendency to function in this direction favors the hypnotic relationship. Such patients may be aware of this functioning. On the other hand, they may give it little thought although it is observed easily by the therapist. The types of statements involved find illustration in comments by a patient who had the probably unusual experience of an incestuous relationship with her brother during the course of her hypnoanalysis (Schneck, 25). Regarding her sexual impulses and conflict, with related feelings of guilt, she said while in hypnosis, "Sometimes I feel I want to be desexed, not to feel anything at all, not to have any feelings or urges. I guess that's why I don't feel so guilty about masturbating. It's a way to satisfy in a private way the feelings I don't want to recognize." Later she said, "I think maybe one of the reaons I feel in some ways comfortable about being at home now is that my father treats me like I'm sexless, just his daughter. We haven't discussed sex and he doesn't make comments about my friends, although he worries where I go. I feel he accepts me. It's this sexless feeling I wish I could attain. It takes the pressure off a little bit."

6. Perceptiveness and Patients' Attitudes toward Hypnotic Experience

Patients are encountered who function well in hypnosis, deal with significant material, experience therapeutic improvement, yet fail to appreciate consciously with any consistency their facility in utilizing the hypnotic setting itself. Awareness of favorable change is expressed spontaneously from time to time but the impression they give is that consciousness of the favorable trend in hypnoanalytic developments is suppressed often, and at times in fact repressed. There may be many reasons to account for this. Frequently encountered is the patient who functions this way as part of a marked obsessive-compulsive personality pattern. Such a patient often focusses attention on technical aspects of hypnotic activity and on specific hypnotic phenomena he wishes to experience in order to feel that he is indeed a good hypnotic subject. This serves part of his defensive needs by which he relegates the idea, need, and energy output for therapeutic change to a secondary position.

A fifty year old man with pronounced obsessive-compulsive attributes was especially interested in modifying his compulsive approaches to interpersonal relations, and in allaying concurrent anxiety in business and social settings. His hypnoanalytic sessions were handled favorably, but his defense against recognizing the significance of some observations during hypnosis was the frequently observed obsessive concern with the issue of "hypnotic depth," replaced later with emphasis on his possible ability to achieve posthypnotic amnesias. Although at times one may accede to the patient's desire to "perform well" by centering attention on such concerns, they may frequently be by-passed once the patient is really involved emotionally in his therapeutic work. Eventually, however, they should be analyzed because of their representation of fundamental behavioral qualities and modes of thinking as part of over-all personality functioning. The patient just alluded to was inordinately concerned with the problem of control with various associated magical connotations. Manipulation of "depth" and memory functioning fit into this framework.

Such patients are much less perceptive than others of the fine points in their hypnotic activities which have therapeutic significance, theoretical interest, and which serve to extend an awareness of the richness of hypnotic behavior. For the patient and therapist, the first point dealing with therapeutic advance is of primary importance. But the last point often serves to raise the level of self-confidence in a patient, especially when his hypnotic functioning is an index to him of his ability to "do well" in general. Perceptiveness of the type just mentioned may occur often in patients who are not unduly taken by technical issues of hypnotic procedure and who are not intent on having dramatic or unusual experiences in hypnosis. Regression and revivification often fall into the latter category as far as patients are concerned, and indeed as are many therapists.

7. Regression and Revivification in Hypnoanalysis

A patient, fifty-four years old, experienced episodes of revivification in the course of a hypnoanalysis. The highly dramatic manifestations usually expected of such experiences were lacking. During certain sessions there had been periods of silence during which the patient appeared to be having emotional reactions judging by some alterations of facial expression and the slightest of body movements. In describing afterwards what had occurred, she revealed that regression had taken place to earlier age levels, and that as this happened spontaneously she retained a bare thread of contact with her environment, a contact so subtle it was difficult for her to describe. As the intense reliving of past happenings continued on this level, she did not communicate with the analyst. After temporal and special reorientation took place, she was able to describe the hypnotic events. From other observations it can be said that this type of hypnotic behavior is not rare, but it does require on the part of the patient a significant element of perceptiveness regarding inner experience, and the ability of the patient to communicate in this way in order for such analytic events to be appreciated fully by the therapist. These events take place sufficiently frequently for the doctor to suspect their presence at times, on the basis of his clinical background. In the absence of these essentials, this type of spontaneous revivification is easily overlooked (Scheck, 26). Such revivifications are devoid of verbalizations in the present or even past tense, extensive motor involvements, and expression of intense emotion concurrent with the experience. The particular patient just referred to was unable to speak at such times. This hypnoanalytic functioning was observed originally in patients who regressed and revivified happenings of pre-verbal age levels. I was able to validate and describe its occurrence after several patients had offered similar descriptions.

Some revivified happenings in the case of the above mentioned patient pertained to childhood and adolescent periods. When she was twelve years old, in bed with her father, she had sexual sensations that precipitated an anxiety reaction. In the hypnoanalysis this came through with great emotional impact. On another occasion her mother was singing a song that was associated for the patient with fear of abandonment. She reacted accordingly.

Additional settings had to do with early dating experience, death of a brother, loss of her dog, a whipping by her father, and other events. This patient used the term "vivification" in her description and accounted for it by the claim that the happenings seemed more real and emotionally intense than the original events. I should suspect that in the real life happenings, repressive forces were set in motion rapidly in an effort to cope with overwhelming stress stimuli. Full awareness of the internal and external milieu was not possible. In retrieving the occurrences and integrating them into consciousness, the feeling of greater reality ensued. This tends to be consistent with what I have observed and described in other patients as the acquisition during treatment of emotional insight preceding intellectual insight, the reverse of what is so often mentioned in connection with traditional psychoanalytic settings. I think the role of the transference relationship contributes to the impression of greater reality described for the hypnoanalytic event. For example, with this patient the analyst was identified in part with her father. The current identification, as part of the transference, merging with the other elements in the revivification lends further, I am inclined to believe, to the feeling of greater reality as already described.

The range of experience in regression and revivification is, in my opinion, much broader than is generally appreciated, and the settings, circumstances, and fine points in interpersonal relations influence the manifestations of personality expression at such times. To expect stereotyped reactions with conformity to well established patterns can blind the observer to an appreciation of the richness of hypnotic experience. One may observe considerable overlapping at times in clinical and experimental settings for the study of regression, but the diversity of possible reactions too should make one aware that differences in behavior do not necessarily invalidate the findings of others. The differences may frequently be accounted for on the basis of spontaneous behavioral participation of the subject or patient, and the special forms of attention by the subject, patient, experimenter, or hypnoanalyst. For pertinent comparisons in this area, the writings of Kline (27, 28), Guze (29), and McCranie and Crasilneck (30) may be consulted.

8. The Concept of Dynamic Hypnotic Age Regression

As is well known, many studies dealing with hypnotic regression have been published. Some have attempted to integrate Rorschach explorations with personality studies and hypnosis. A good example for our purposes is that of Bergmann, Graham and Leavitt who reported on Rorschach exploration of consecutive hypnotic chronological age level regression (38). A series of Rorschach tests were given to a hypnotically regressed subject. Consecutive chronological age levels were studied. This subject was a soldier with conversion hysteria. He was described as having an "inadequately resolved oedipal situation." He was very dependent on his father while harboring strong unconscious hostility, and there were incestuous tendencies toward his mother. There was a history of phobias, nightmares, and compulsive rituals. The Rorschach findings showed changes at regressed age levels that followed closely the clinical data available. Such longitudinal personality analysis was believed to have diagnostic and therapeutic value.

I think studies such as this have implications for the practice of hypnoanalysis. In research settings such procedures can be integrated into the total procedural features of a hypnoanalysis although objections may be raised regarding possible interference with the normal progress of treatment. There are additional implications regarding effects on the transference relationship, but of course this is to be expected as are the effects of any change in procedures that have previously been uniform. Utilization of such studies are less likely to occur in private practice areas, but of course the results of the studies can influence the development of hypnoanalytic practice in general regardless of its setting. Similar and related studies involve, for example, hypnotic ablation techniques for the study of personality development (39) and Rorschach content in hypnosis with chronological age level regressions (40). I have referred elsewhere to many studies dealing with psychological testing procedures and hypnosis, and there would be little purpose in repeating details now (Schneck, 41). The theme we should focus on at present pertains to the stress on chronological age level regressions and the nature of hypnotic regression as such, with its implications for hypnoanalytic efforts. Specifically, I have in my work made a point of the importance of what I have designated "dynamic hypnotic age regression" (42).

When investigations of hypnotic age regression are reviewed, it seems that the idea of total or complete regression fascinates the investigators. The question that arises is how far must one go to achieve this ultimate stage. Obviously some things cannot be achieved. Gross structural designs will not be altered. Body size will not change, though behavior can be modified. In line with this I think that concern with exact chronological duplication is misleading and impedes understanding if an all or nothing view is adopted as a goal for authenticity. It is not a measure of validity. It is too static. Regression is affected by many variables that include hypnotic technique, a subject's changing psychological set, hypnotic capacities, and the dynamic significance of various age periods for the particular subject or patient.

I favor regression to the indefinite past in hypnoanalytic work. Patients are permitted to be spontaneous in achieving age levels significant for them within the framework of issues and conflicts of special importance to them at the moment. The levels selected are consistent this way with inner psychological forces striving toward elimination of conflict. I believe that such spontaneous choice by patients in hypnoanalysis, and in other settings too, is generally more impressive behaviorally, dynamically, and therapeutically. If one specifies age levels to be attained experimentally, negative or unimpressive results may ensue as a result of the generation of psychological forces that oppose a more natural, meaningful, and spontaneous psychological movement within the subjects or patients.

In hypnoanalysis, regression to specific age periods that may be of little personal meaning to patients tends to be essentially unproductive. Regression to highly charged age levels are more likely to occur spontaneously when the hypnoanalyst allows the patient much lattitude. These regressions are more impressive, and are psychologically meaningful revivifications. More artificially suggested chronological age level regressions often stimulate only simple recall. Revivifications tend more to be intense, especially in cases such as amnesias involving delimited, psychological pressure areas.

I think a most significant finding is the experience of reliving different time periods at the same moment so that a temporal setting pertinent to one age level may fuse, for example, with a spacial setting pertinent to another. Also, affective and intellectual experience separated in time may merge with strange affinity. I believe this fusion takes place because of the dynamic relatedness of the settings and the time periods, and it is surprising how often such situations are valuable therapeutically. This type of fusion, in the light of more conventional views of regression, may prompt the conclusion that the regression is invalid and the experimental results negative. Obviously different chronological levels are involved. Yet in psychiatric treatment settings, chronological levels chosen by the therapist may turn out to be absurdly insignificant, whereas the spontaneous dynamic hypnotic age level regressions may be very important for the patient. I think such regressions are also more natural phenomena psychologically and, in a broader context, biologically. Failure or success in the induction of hypnotic regression thus assumes proportions even more complex than has been generally recognized, and I have continued to be inclined toward this view during the several years of hypnoanalytic practice since I first proposed the idea of dynamic regression. The spacial-temporal distortion mentioned above and the fusion of time periods is not only psychologically instructive, but also consistent with this concept of dynamic hypnotic age regression as distinguished from chronological hypnotic age regression. The dynamic concept covers more thoroughly the recognition of spontaneity and psychological fluidity and change in hypnotic subjects and patients studied from longitudinal and cross-sectional perspectives.

While dealing with this aspect of regression, I think it would be pertinent to mention the existence of some studies in hypnotic "progression." Kline offered a case study wherein the progression state revealed a decline in mental ability that assumed a pattern like that reported in clinical studies of aging (43). With Guze he declares that work involving the H-T-P techniques and the O'Rourke Vocabulary Test showed impressive alterations in a subject's drawings and vocabulary during the hypnotic states whereas simulation attempts failed to achieve this for regression and progression (44). Should there be further substantiation of such findings, I think the elements involved will be effectively integrated with the themes I have mentioned in connection with dynamic regression. It is important to note at this point that progression techniques have not played a significant role up until now in hypnoanalytic investigations although one cannot say as yet what the future holds in connection with such studies.

9. Hypnotic Hallucinatory Experience

The issue of dynamic ties can be illustrated further in relation to other techniques. A patient, who was being studied hypnoanalytically, was passing through an exploratory phase that allowed some work to be done with auditory hallucinations (Schneck, 45). Distinctions were drawn between imagined conversations and hallucinated conversations. Persons to be hallucinated were selected at times by the hypnoanalyst and on occasions the patient was permitted spontaneous choice. Some of her experiences were intense and entailed considerable show of emotion. Others were less emotionally intense. She differentiated between words heard from within herself and those she identified as emanating from external sources. Here again, as in the case of dynamic regression, spacial and temporal elements were divorced from their conventional relationships. They were distorted in keeping with psychodynamic needs. The effects of the latter can be illustrated by examining her reactions. The beginning of hallucinatory behavior did not set a pattern for continuous similar activity. Responsive behavior varied from time to time. A hallucinatory episode might be succeeded by imagined conversation even though the instructions given to the patient remained the same. She could hallucinate people already dead. Her aunt, for example, had died twenty years before. Her deceased mother could be hallucinated but she was unable to do this with her husband who was living at the time and with whom there was much conflict. Responses involving her daughter entailed complex elements.

Studies of hypnotic hallucinatory activity, aside from their intrinsic interest for personality investigations in general, should be helpful in attempts to understand the hallucinations of psychotic patients. It must be noted, however, that hypnoanalytic work specifically has been less extensive with psychotic patients than with others although the use of induced hallucinatory measures as such have played a role in some hypnoanalytic investigations (Schneck, 46-48).

10. Spontaneous Nocturnal Dreams, Hypnotic Dreams, and Hypnoanalysis

In a certain sense, many hypnotic techniques that differ in appearance or on first impression, entail elements in common as far as their potential impact on the patient is concerned. Induced hallucinations offer an opening for mention of hypnotic dreams at this point because of some parallel influences, although the nature of the patient's experiences differs somewhat within the framework of the two types of functioning. Kanzer mentioned, in regard to hypnotic dreams, that in these induced dreams the voice of the hypnotist substitutes for the day's residues. His ideas mold the latent thoughts. His comments generate the dream wish. The primary process during dream formation elaborates these elements, permitting the patient's unconscious responses to these forces to receive expression (49). Kanzer described a twenty-one year old soldier with hysterical dyskinesia, treated with the use of hypnosis, and claimed that hypnotic dreams were of value in establishing contact with this passive person. Aspects of dream psychology were revealed which were considered to be of theoretical and practical value (50).

There are, of course, differences of opinion regarding the nature and implications of hypnotic dreams. This can, in turn, influence the wish to utilize them as part of hypnoanalysis and it can affect the manner in which they are dealt with when used in hypnoanalytic settings. Brenman, for example, questioned the assumption that the hypnotic dream duplicates in function or structure the spontaneous night dream. She noted the wide range of response to the hypnotic suggestion for dreaming. The average production seemed to have a structure that was intermediate between the daydream and spontaneous night dream. Primary processes were used more than in ordinary waking thought but less than in what she called a typical night dream. A further note was made to the effect that hypnotic dreams in a series may progressively clarify the defensive aspect of a conflict or the impulse that is being defended against (51).

I think a frequent error lies in the comparison of the productions of one patient or subject with those of another, ignoring comparisons between hypnotic productions of one individual with spontaneous productions of the same individual. For example, when the hypnotic dreams of a patient appear to resemble what might be called ordinary daydreams, it may be discovered that his spontaneous nocturnal dreams give the same impression. I had occasion to prepare a book chapter on clinical and experimental aspects of hypnotic dreams, stressing my own work and focussing special attention on four papers by others. One was the item by Brenman that I have just mentioned. The others were by Farber and Fisher (52), Regardie (53), and Mazer (54). For readers especially interested in this, I might add that the entire subject and discussion has reference also to earlier work by Schrötter (55), Roffenstein (56), and Nachmansohn (57), and, of course, to the basic work of Freud (58). It seemed to me that hypnotic dreams differ in certain ways from spontaneous nocturnal dreams in regard to function. The differences stem from the settings involved, the nature of technical devices that are employed, such as the hypnotic induction processes, with their psychological implications for subjects, patients, experimenters and therapists, and issues having to do with complexities of interpersonal contacts including resistance and transference conceins. All of this has obvious implications for hypnoanalysis. Beyond this it remained my impression that allowing for comparisons of spontaneous hypnotic and nocturnal dreams derived from the same subjects and patients, the structure of such dreams is apparently essentially similar (Schneck, 72).

Much of the literature on hypnotic dreams pertains to such dreams induced on suggestions by hypnotherapists. In hypnoanalysis, if one were to claim that onset of such dreams is the result of implied suggestion whether or not specific verbal suggestions are given, the fact remains that hypnotic dreams are reported apparently spontaneously. Often, patients offering dream material do not refer to it as a dream, hypnotic or otherwise. They present the content as visualizations, without using this term, or as daydreams, employing this term perhaps most frequently. It may be observed at times that the appearance of the patients suggests greater absorption in, and involvement with the hypnosis when they are dreaming. Not infrequently, patients claim they feel they are in a deeper hypnosis during such dreaming. The nature of the hypnotic dream material is related to the total psychological equilibrium of the patient at that point, and to changing aspects of this equilibrium over a period of time. This is in turn connected with the alterations in hypnotic depth observed by hypnoanalysts in patients during any one session and over a series of sessions. Brenman, Gill and Knight (59) discussed the hypothesis concerning change in depth when an existing psychological equilibrium is threatened. They felt that the hypnotic state incorporates the gratification of pregenital and oedipal libidinal needs and changing balance between these needs, expression of hostility, and defenses against these instinctual impulses.

11. Hypnotic Imagery and Sensory and Motor Phenomena during Hypnoanalysis

Alterations in hypnotic depth, as mentioned here, are related not only to hypnotic dreams, but to other forms of experience such as aforementioned spontaneous sensory and motor phenomena occurring during hypnosis. These phenomena may be accompanied by visual imagery, in fact related imagery during hypnosis. A twenty-eight year old woman experienced a variety of such phenomena during her hypnoanalysis. One sensory phenomenon entailed her feeling of being on a "slant." When she mentioned this the first time she though of a staircase on a yacht owned by her family when she was a child. She felt herself rocking back and forth and this stopped when the boat stopped rocking. Her mental images continued to develop further, leading to the view of stairs that in turn were associated with her brother's warning, when she was a child, that she would be grabbed by a man at the head of the staircase at home. This led to the memory, possibly a false memory of being fondled and kissed by her uncle, again when she was a child and on a staircase, with her reaction of shock at that time. There was a concurrent memory of coming down a staircase, as a child, and seeing her mother kissing her uncle.

Hypnotic fantasies can furnish significant clues to psycho-pathology whether or not they accompany sensory and motor phenomena as mentioned above. A forty-five year old man mani-fested delayed eye closure during induction, but following closure he made exaggerated but unsuccessful attempts to open his eyes. Subsequently, in later sessions, this was replaced by his opening his mouth widely during induction. It would happen again and again. Then his eyes would close spasmodically and the jaw move-ments would stop. The jaw movements appeared to be a symbolic counteraction of eye closure. The jaw movements seemed con-sistent with his great hostility and the delayed eye closure a reflection of his ambivalence toward the hypnotic procedure that he had specifically sought.

During several sessions he complained about pains in his eyes. "I don't know what it is—but the eyes, as though I had a pain in the eyes. I don't know. As though something is poking into my eyes. Like a skull with no eyes. (What would be like a skull with no eyes?) My mother used to talk about my father. His eyes were very deep. Comment about his small eyes. His skull would be outlined on his forehead or something like that. Like eyes being pushed back in their sockets. (Whose eyes?) My own eyes. (Pause) As though I was guilty of seeing something I shouldn't have seen and should see. Just trying to see if I could have seen something. (He wondered about viewing intercourse between his mother and father. He used to hear noise as if they were fighting.) I see arrows of light or flashes shooting through my eyes. (Pause) I think of a dress with dazzling lights on it. (Long pause) The desire to com-mit suicide. To die. The curse. 'You should be buried.' My mother said it often to my father. I think of spears and again arrows in the shape of spears going into the head—the skull. (The hypnosis was deepened.) I see the skull with worms crawling all over it. Instead of the face of a—(a person toward whom the patient had mixed feelings) I see this skull."

Although this patient had considerable anxiety and gave the impression of being disturbed in ordinary interviews, his pre-psychotic and potentially explosive status was indicated clearly in these hypnotic fantasies (Schneck, 60). Sometimes patients seeking hypnoanalysis are not obviously disturbed to this degree in introductory non-hypnotic sessions. The hypnoanalytic interviews highlight the disturbance more pointedly. In such cases decisions must be made regarding continued use of hypnosis or relinquishing it in favor of non-hypnotic sessions if it is felt that potential explosiveness can be better contained this way. Problems set in when some patients insist not only on the use of hypnosis, but on elaborate or involved techniques about which they have heard. The hypnoanlyst must use his clinical judgment regarding the course of action. This is based on his general experience with psychotherapy and his specialized experience with hypnosis. Easing of tensions may be achieved with hypnotic methods that are essentially supportive and reassuring rather than exploratory. They may become exploratory at a later date if ego strength has first increased considerably over a period of time.

The hypnotic imagery revealed by the patient mentioned above was especially interesting and additional examples are as follows. "I think of two hands—like sculpted hands, just below the wrist, bent over back to back, on a base. The hands start groping and twisting, trying to face each other. Now flowers grow out of them. Evil flowers. I don't know why they are evil. I think of snakes and people I don't like. Now my eyes hurt. Somebody's sticking things into them. Somebody's trying to choke me, or I'm trying to choke someone. A woman's breast. A railroad track. Legs lying on the track. A funnel. I see hands everywhere. Hands like snakes. I see a patch-quilt with different colors. This eye pains me. *Someone is poking in my eyes!*" At this point in his verbalizations, the patient was panting.

On another occasion he felt his entire body was being squeezed and he had a fantasy of being bound down by ropes. Sometimes he felt pains in the back of his head. He felt his head was being pressed under water, with fingers forced against his neck. He also had feelings of floating on water. He had a fantasy of someone twisting off his penis. His ambivalence toward treatment, the homosexual transference, the extreme masochism, emerged with remarkable clarity in his vivid imagery. The fantasies offer insights into general personality patterns and psychopathology and assist in diagnosis while supplying valuable clues for the conduct of treatment and clues to prognosis. Often patients who reveal such evidence of psychopathology as delineated here may, in non-hypnotic sessions, be quite deceiving in the facade presented. While the hypnotic setting is helpful in revealing the severity of personality disturbance, it carries with it obvious needs for caution and good judgment in decisions emerging from what is gleaned at such times.

12. Applicability and Efficacy of Hypnotic Techniques

When significant findings in hypnosis are revealed with great clarity, there is the temptation to believe that the hypnotic methods used may prove consistently helpful with most, if not all patients. The temptation should be avoided. It can be very misleading. Methods highly effective for one patient may not be so for another. Imagery techniques may do well for a patient at one point in treatment but not at another, or they may do well for some patients consistently but not for others at any time. This may be said of hypnotic automatic writing, for example, or for any other therapeutic method (Schneck, 61). The more recent use of sensory hypnoplasty may prove to be helpful in some hypnoanalytic experiences but I doubt that those employing it will find it to be helpful over a period of time with increasing regularity (62). Various techniques have been most helpful in understanding personality problems or in assisting patients when they have been given concentrated attention, particularly in time-limited contacts, but it might be impractical to attempt to use them reasonably consistently for one patient after another in a full psychotherapeutic schedule as usually obtains in private practice settings. The hypnoanalyst, however, should be familiar with the methods in the event that application appears warranted even occasionally, or rarely. Examples of such measures include hypnotic induction of experimental neuroses and complexes and artificial conflicts (63-65). Play therapy (66) is another, and it does not seem to me that it is used frequently in hypnoanalysis. Materials appropriate to the treatment situation, especially if regression measures are used, must be on hand for it. I employed it within the setting of a mental health clinic where children were seen as frequently as adults for diagnosis and treatment, but private practice situations are usually not conducive to such an approach unless, again, children and adults are seen with sufficient frequency to allow for appropriate therapeutic materials to be available. The acting out that occurs in drama techniques is generally seen with greater consistency in the war neuroses and is appropriate for the hypnoanalysis of soldiers and veterans for whom wartime experiences played significant roles.

As I have intimated on a number of occasions, although patients vary in the techniques they utilize best, visual imagery measures are most frequently amenable to incorporation within a hypnoanalysis and such measures can be combined with other procedures. For example, scene visualization can be combined with word association tests by encouraging imagery responses instead of word responses. Visual imagery in hypnosis in the form of a scene visualization technique as employed in hypnoanalysis may be combined with the Word Association Test and incorporated into such therapy. It can be used for patients functioning in classically light, medium, as well as deep hypnotic states as graded by the formal scales used for such purposes. Actually, any meaningful stimulus word list may substitute for a standard word association test. Imagery responses to stimulus words reveal at times transition states from visualized scenes to hypnotic dreams. Such productions if obtained early in treatment can supply meaningful and helpful clues for further exploration in the hypnoanalysis (Schneck and Kline, 67).

13. Diagnostic Categories and Amenability to Hypnoanalysis

Returning to an over-all view of hypnoanalysis, the question arises as to the types of problems, from a diagnostic point of view, that are most amenable to this therapeutic approach (Schneck, 31). I am inclined to feel that the general trend in likelihood for improvement would essentially follow the trend for therapies in which hypnosis does not play a role. However, one must take into consideration, as is obviously implied in all of the foregoing discussion, that within this trend the introduction of the hypnotic setting offers possibilities of additional opportunities for some patients to experience added benefit beyond that supplied by non-hypnotic psychotherapy.

One clinician has suggested that conditions responding best to hypnoanalysis are the traumatic neuroses, conversion hysteria, some forms of anxiety hysteria, and alcoholism (32). Probably for alcoholism there would be more differing opinions than would hold for the other problems. On the basis of my experience I should rate highly the hysterical disorders and some character neuroses (Schneck, 33). The obsessive-compulsive problems are usually less amenable although a firm ruling should be avoided because of the exceptions one encounters. Needless to say, much depends on the special experience of the hypnoanalysts and their individual preferences. For example, most would not be inclined to favor work with schizophrenic patients, yet the few therapists working intensively in this way, while experienced also with the use of hypnosis, can be expected to be much more successful than other therapists for this category of patients. Bowers (34) has claimed, in this connection, that the strain on therapists is great, but she feels that hypnosis has been helpful in dealing with the hostile and ambivalent, deep, dependent transference. She has stated that patients with this additional help are apparently brought more quickly to social remission. Psychopaths and border-line problems are included in this evaluation (34).

There is a tendency still to consider hypnotic methods as applicable especially, if effective at all, to disorders of an hysterical nature primarily. The reason for this is emphasis on the mechanism of repression closely identified with hysterical problems. The trend toward a broader and more complex hypnoanalytic procedure with allowance for considerable use of free association in the hypnotic setting, and the extensive use of visual imagery techniques to further self-evaluation, has resulted, for the types of sessions I have conducted, in elucidating the operation of other dynamisms. These include identification, isolation, symbolization, introjection, projection, displacement, rationalization, and condensation.

14. Anxiety and Hypnoanalysis

The use of hypnosis, often with stress on relaxation methods, is well suited to many patients for the relief of anxiety. I have discussed elsewhere certain aspects of acute and chronic anxiety (Schneck, 68). The degree of such relief varies among patients

(Schneck, 35). This effect is often of help in hypnoanalysis, especially in early stages when anxiety is presented as an initial complaint and when the patient feels relief is virtually a necessity to ensure meaningful cooperation in more extensive therapeutic work. Some good results can be achieved often regardless of the length of time the anxiety has been in evidence. When patients express the wish for anxiety reduction in this way, the results can, when successful, cement a favorable initial transference and expedite progress in the hypnoanalysis as it gets under way. Also, interpersonal relationships in general are eased to a point of making the patient much more comfortable. If too much relief is obtained in the face of inadequate motivation for treatment on other grounds, premature termination may take place. In so far as possible, the hypnoanalyst must bear this in mind and conduct sessions carefully on the basis of his surmise about the personality of his patient.

A twenty-eight year old woman, seeking treatment because of problems with her children and for promiscuous behavior, had been led to believe that the use of hypnosis could assist her with the anxiety she was experiencing. Her wish for relief in this connection was gratified in one early hypnosis session, following which exploration on non-hypnotic levels ensued during several subsequent interviews. Finally, the hypnotic setting was introduced again as she moved into hypnoanalytic work. In some cases of this type, any insistence on postponing the use of hypnosis for initial relief may reenforce resistances to treatment in general, result in premature termination of contacts, and possibly forestall proper efforts by the patient to obtain meaningful help elsewhere.

It is not unusual to encounter patients who express disappointment with earlier contacts in psychotherapy and analysis. They stress simplified techniques now for symptom relief with special reference to anxiety. When initial benefits are obtained in hypnotherapy, such patients are often amenable to, and desirous of further work on a hypnoanalytic basis. Needless to say, the results in attempts to reduce anxiety are linked to transference issues present at this time. These issues need not be clarified immediately although elucidation may be achieved rapidly in some cases. When treatment develops into a hypnoanalysis, analysis of the transference becomes a significant element in the therapeutic contact.

In the reduction of anxiety under conditions just described, pressure tactics are avoided as I believe they should be in all settings where stress is placed on individual symptoms. If a patient feels better and terminates treatment soon thereafter, his continued well being will depend on many forces at play including his inherent ego strength and adaptive capacities that are conducive to healthy psychological reorganization. Symptom relief under any circumstance is generally difficult to achieve, but meaningful personality changes, concurrent with such relief and symptom disappearance do occur more often than is generally recognized (Schneck, 36).

15. The Concept of Assurance of Illness Reversibility

As part of over-all resistance to treatment, some patients demonstrate what I have described as the need for assurance of illness reversibility (Schneck, 37). A major goal in treatment seems to be the assuring themselves about the reversibility of their illnesses. When they feel satisfied on this score, they terminate treatment. Part of the total problem involves the apparent retention of symptoms for secondary gain. Termination may take place soon after treatment is initiated or it may be delayed. Some degree of improvement takes place prior to the break in contact. Reasons offered by patients for giving up treatment are inconsistent with information supplied earlier by them. An example is the claim of financial difficulties. Clarification of such occurrences is possible especially in hypnotherapy, but this need by patients mainly to assure themselves about reversibility of their illnesses is widespread, I should say, in many areas of medical practice.

A case in point is a middle aged woman, dissatisfied with previous general medical and psychiatric contacts, seeking relief from hot flushes during her menopause. She was shy, insecure, and self-conscious. She believed the reddening of her face was noticed by others. She worked efficiently but avoided contact with people as much as possible in business settings. Relief was experienced early in treatment at which time she was being prepared also for more extensive evaluations and understandings of her problems. When she attempted to discontinue prematurely and was engaged in a discussion of this move, she was able to substantiate spontaneously the observations outlined above. She confirmed the fact that having proved to herself that improvement could occur, she felt impelled to discontinue. This patient was rather masochistic, as became quite evident to her in time. The total picture of her maneuvers was rather consistent, but it was fortunate that she was ultimately able to get herself to continue therapeutic efforts. She became involved in a more extensive hypnoanalysis and made worthwhile gains. This patient could be counted among those who are exceptions to the rule. Those who demonstrate the reaction just described do not return for follow-through in treatment. When they establish psychiatric contacts again, they are likely to involve new doctors with whom their pattern is undoubtedly repeated.

The ability to achieve symptom relief with hypnotherapy, whether it be within the framework of a broader hypnoanalysis or not, seems to favor gaining a more clear-cut impression of the issue of assurance of illness reversibility. A man in his forties suffered gastrointestinal distress requiring careful attention to eating habits. It was a chronic problem for which he had been examined medically on many occasions and treated unsuccessfully. Prior analysis had not helped him at all. Despite his alleged reluctance to explore the problem psychodynamically, he proceeded to talk in detail about such previous investigations while asserting his wish for simple symptom removal. He was loud and pseudo-aggressive as he seemed to attempt to deny in this way his feelings of weakness and dependency. He cooperated in hypnotic induction technique, obtained no improvement at first, and did not hesitate to mention this. Then his comments ceased and inquiry had to be made regarding any progress, whereupon it was learned that indeed he was experiencing symptom relief. Soon thereafter, having begun to achieve the goals he had defiantly demanded, he discontinued treatment, claiming he would, in a fashion quite contradictory, seek help through the very routine medical channels he had deplored until then as having been quite unable to assist him despite extensive studies and treatment efforts.

16. Limitations on Symptom Relief, and Anxiety-depression Correlations

When hypnoanalysis is initiated, it appears desirable at times to achieve at least a measure of symptomatic relief before embarking on more extensive investigations. Patients demand this at times, but not always. Even when they do not insist, their needs for physical and psychological comfort point in this direction.

Many therapists completely devoted to insight therapy in the sense of making the unconscious conscious, or its equivalent in other terminology, stress the fact that symptomatic relief is not sufficient. There must be more. And investigative techniques will supply this, they say, and effect additional symptomatic change that lesser suggestive measures will not provide. I do not share this devotion, and my clinical experience denies the aforementioned claims as they relate at least to some cases. My concern with investigative techniques in general, hypnoanalysis in terms of special interest, and psychoanalytic as the major orientation, does not negate the fact that certain patients can achieve symptomatic, partial relief, without additional investigations proving capable of enhancing these therapeutic benefits through acquisition of significant insights. For example, hypnotherapeutic measures eased significantly the discomfort of a patient with achalasia of the esophagus (Schneck, 69). This measure of relief was not extended, however, by continued examination of personality functioning and problems with and without the employment of hypnoanalytic settings. Strong masochistic components were evident in his character make-up. A significant sexual episode, preceding the onset of his symptoms, was examined, as were many other elements in his sexual history and activities. Evaluations were made of deprivation of parental love and his limited capacities for experiencing deep affection. Symbolic significances of food and eating were explored. Self-punitive attributes were assessed. These and related concerns were studied, but whatever he derived in a general sense from this work was not matched by any symptomatic relief beyond what he had already sustained.

Needless to say, when symptomatic relief is attempted (Schneck, 70), whether or not it is achieved, consideration must be given to the anxiety bound and expressed in the symptom manifestations, and with this concern about the anxiety there should be given concurrently some attention to the presence of depression, hidden or apparent. Frequently, the clear presence of anxiety tends to hide the depression, and the reverse is often true too (Schneck, 71).

When they are discerned concurrently, the full impact of each is sometimes obscured, so that relief from one may be accompanied by a seeming though not necessarily an actual increase in the other. This must be kept in mind in all therapeutic efforts, psychotherapeutic and pharmacotherapeutic too. This relationship between anxiety and depression, noted here, comes into view often in the course of hypnoanalytic work.

References

1. Schneck, J. M.: Hypnosis and the productive orientation. *Dis. Nerv. Syst.*, *12:*241, 1951.
2. Fromm, E.: *Man For Himself, An Inquiry Into the Psychology of Ethics.* New York, Rinehart, 1947.
3. Schneck, J. M.: Relationships between hypnotist-audience and hypnotist-subject interaction. *Int. J. Clin. Exp. Hyp.*, *6:*171, 1958.
4. Wells, W. R.: A basic deception in exhibitions of hypnosis. *J. Abnorm. Soc. Psychol.*, *41:*145, 1946.
5. Schneck, J. M.: A military offense induced by hypnosis. *J. Nerv. Ment. Dis.*, *106:*186, 1947.
6. Bramwell, J. M.: *Hypnotism: Its History, Practice and Theory.* London, William Rider and Son, Ltd., 1921.
7. Rowland, L. W.: Will hypnotized persons try to harm themselves or others? *J. Abnorm. Soc. Psychol.*, *34:*114, 1939.
8. Wells, W. R.: Experiments in the hypnotic production of crime. *J. Psychol.*, *11:*63, 1941.
9. Young, P. C.: Hypnotism. *Psychol. Bull.*, *23:*504, 1926.
10. Estabrooks, G. H.: The possible antisocial use of hypnotism, in Schneck, J. M., Editor: *Hypnosis and Personality.* New York, Grune and Stratton, 1951.
11. Reiter, P. J.: *Antisocial or Criminal Acts and Hypnosis.* Copenhagen, Munksgaard, 1958.
12. Schneck, J. M.: A note on a special hypnotic situation within a medico-disciplinary setting. *Brit. J. Med. Hyp.*, *4:*12, Autumn 1952.
13. Schneck, J. M.: The unconscious relationship between hypnosis and death. *Psychoanal. Rev.*, *38:*271, 1951.
14. Gilman, T. T., and Marcuse, F. L.: Animal hypnosis. *Psychol. Bull.*, *46:*151, 1949.
15. Poe, E. A.: *Tales.* London, Oxford University Press, no date.
16. Du Maurier, G.: *Trilby.* New York, Harper, 1894.

17. Schneck, J. M.: Hypnoanalytic Elucidation of the Hypnosis-Death Concept. *Psychiat. Quart., Supp. 24:*286, 1950.
18. Lundholm, H.: Laboratory neuroses. *Character and Personality,* 2:127, 1933.
19. Schneck, J. M.: A note on spontaneous hallucinations during hypnosis. *Psychiat. Quart.,* 24:492, 1950.
20. Schneck, J. M.: Spontaneous homonymous hemianopsia in hypnotic imagery. *Brit. J. Med. Hyp.,* 2:2, Spring 1951.
21. Schneck, J. M.: Psychogenic Visual Disturbances. *New York J. Med., 59:*2031, May 15, 1959.
22. Dunbar, H. F.: *Emotions and Bodily Changes.* New York, Columbia Universtiy Press, 1938.
23. Fenichel, O.: *Psychoanalytic Theory of Neuroses.* New York, W. W. Norton, 1945
24. Freud, S.: Psychogenic visual disturbances according to psychoanalytical conceptions, in *Collected Papers.* London, Hogarth Press, 1946, Vol. 2.
25. Schneck, J. M.: Incest experience during hypnoanalysis. *Int. J. Clin. Exp. Hyp.,* 8:147, 1960.
26. Schneck, J. M.: Special aspects of hypnotic regression and revivification. *Int. J. Clin. Exp. Hyp.,* 8:37, 1960.
27. Kline, M. V.: Hypnotic age regression and intelligence. *J. Genet. Psychol.,* 77:129, 1950.
28. Kline, M. V.: Childhood fears in relation to hypnotic age regression. A case report. *J. Genet. Psychol.,* 82:137, 1953.
29. Kline, M. V., and Guze, H.: The use of a drawing technique in the investigation of hypnotic age regression and progression. *Brit. J. Med. Hyp.,* 3:10, 1951.
30. McCranie, E. J., and Crasilneck, H. B.: The conditioned reflex in hypnotic age regression. *J. Clin. Exp. Psychopath.,* 16:120, 1955.
31. Schneck, J. M.: Current advances in hypnotherapy. *Amer. J. Psychoth., 11:*408, 1957.
32. Wolberg, L. R.: Psychoanalysis and hypnoanalysis, in Wolff, W.: *Contemporary Psychotherapists Examine Themselves.* Springfield, Ill., Thomas, 1956.
33. Schneck, J. M.: Hypnotherapy, in Wolff, W.: *Contemporary Psychotherapists Examine Themselves.* Springfield, Ill., Thomas, 1956.
34. Bowers, M. K., Berkowitz, B., and Brecher, S.: Hypnosis in severely dependent states. *J. Clin. Exp. Hyp.,* 2:2, 1954.
35. Schneck, J. M.: Hypnotherapy for the control of anxiety. *Dis. Nerv. Syst.,* 14:274, 1953.

36. Schneck, J. M.: Sympton relief, authority substitution, and suggestibility. *Dis. Nerv. Syst.*, *20:*583, 1959.
37. Schneck, J. M.: Concept of assurance of illness reversibility. *Dis. Nerv. Syst.*, *17:*191, 1956.
38. Bergmann, M. S., Graham, H., and Leavitt, H. C.: Rorschach exploration of consecutive hypnotic chronological age level regressions. *Psychosom. Med.*, *9:*20, 1947.
39. Spiegel, H., Shor, J., and Fishman, S.: An Hypnotic ablation technique for the study of personality development. *Psychosom. Med.*, *7:*273, 1945.
40. Mercer, M., and Gibson, R. W.: Rorschach content in hypnosis: chronological age level regression. *J. Clin. Psychol.*, *6:*352, 1950.
41. Schneck, J M.: Hypnosis and clinical psychology, in Brower, D., and Abt, L.: *Progress in Clinical Psychology.* New York, Grune and Stratton, 1956.
42. Schneck, J. M.: Dynamic hypnotic age regression. *Amer. J. Psychiat.*, *113:*178, 1956.
43. Kline, M. V.: Hypnosis and age progression: A case report. *J. Genet. Psychol.*, *78:*195, 1951.
44. Kline, M. V., and Guze, H.: The use of a drawing technique in the investigation of hypnotic age regression and progression. *Brit. J. Med. Hyp.*, *Winter:*1, 1951.
45. Schneck, J. M.: An experimental study of hypnotically induced auditory hallucinations. *J. Clin. Exp. Hyp.*, *2:*163, 1954.
46. Schneck, J. M.: An experimental hypnotherapeutic procedure involving induced auditory hallucinations. *J. Gen. Psychol.*, *50:*155, 1954.
47. Schneck, J. M.: Hypnotic hallucinatory behavior. *J. Clin. Exp. Hyp.*, *1:*4, 1953.
48. Schneck, J. M.: A hypnoanalytic investigation of psychogenic dyspnea with the use of induced auditory hallucinations and special additional hypnotic techniques. *J. Clin. Exp. Hyp.*, *2:*80, 1954.
49. Kanzer, M.: The metapsychology of the hypnotic dream. *Int. J. Psychoanal.*, *34:*part 3, 1953.
50. Kanzer, M.: The therapeutic use of dreams induced by hypnotic suggestion. *Psychoanal. Quart.*, *14:*313, 1945.
51. Brenman, M.: Dreams and hypnosis. *Psychoanal. Quart.*, *18:*455, 1949.
52. Farber, L. H., and Fisher, C.: An experimental approach to dream psychology through the use of hypnosis. *Psychoanal. Quart.*, *12:*202, 1943.
53. Regardie, F. I.: Experimentally induced dreams as psychotherapeutic aids. *Amer. J. Psychoth.*, *4:*643, 1950.
54. Mazer, M.: An experimental study of the hypnotic dream. *Psychiatry: Journal for the Study of Interpersonal Processes*, 14:265, 1951.

55. Schrötter, K.: Experimentelle Träume. *Zbl. Psychoanal.*, *2:*638, 1912.
56. Roffenstein, G.: Experimentelle Symbolträume, ein Beitrag zur Diskussion über die Psychoanalyse. *Z. Ges. Neuropsychiat.*, *87:*362, 1923.
57. Nachmansohn, M.: Über Experimentelle Erzengte Traüme nebst Kritischen Bemerkungen über die Psychoanalytische Methodik (vorläufige milleilung). *Z. Ges. Neuropsychiat.*, *98:*556, 1925.
58. Freud, S.: The interpretation of dreams, in *Basic Writings of Sigmund Freud*. New York, Moden Library, 1938.
59. Brenman, M., Gill, M., and Knight, R. P.: Spontaneous fluctuations in depth of hypnosis and their implications for ego-function. *Int. J. Psychoanal.*, *33:*part 1, 1952.
60. Schneck, J. M.: Spontaneous sensory and motor phenomena with related imagery during hypnosis. *Psychiat. Quart.*, *Supp.:*part 1, 1956.
61. Schneck, J. M.: Hypnotic automatic writing and a proposal for elucidation of unconscious influences in psychological experimentation. *Percept. and Motor Skills*, *13:*58, 1961.
62. Raginsky, B. B.: Sensory hypnoplasty with case illustrations. *Int. J. Clin. Exp. Hyp.*, *10:*205, 1962.
63. Erickson, M. H.: A study of an experimental neurosis hypnotically induced in a case of ejaculatio praecox. *Brit. J. Med. Psychol.*, *15:*34, 1935.
64. Huston, P. E., Shakow, W., and Erickson, M. H.: A study of hypnotically induced complexes by means of the Luria technique. *J. Gen. Psychol.*, *11:*65 1934.
65. McDowell, M.: An abrupt cessation of major neurotic symptoms following an hypnotically induced artificial conflict. *Bull Menninger Clin.*, *12:*168, 1948.
66. Wolberg, L. R.: Hypnosis and psychoanalytic therapy (hypnoanalysis). *Amer. J. Psychother.*, *1:*412, 1947.
67. Schneck, J. M., and Kline, M. V.: Hypnotic scene visualization and the word Association Test. *J. Gen. Psychol.*, *46:*29, 1952.
68. Schneck, J. M.: Classification of anxiety reactions (anxiety states). *J. Nerv. Ment. Dis.*, *103:*81, 1946.
69. Schneck, J. M.: Hypnotherapy for achalasia (cardiospasm). *Amer. J. Psychiat.*, *11:*1042, 1958.
70. Schneck, J. M.: Ichthyosis treated with hypnosis. *Dis. Nerv. Syst.*,*15:* 211, 1954.
71. Schneck, J. M.: Anxiety-depression and pharmacotherapy-psychotherapy correlations. *Amer. J. Psychiat.*, *115:*78, 1958.
72. Schneck, J. M.: Clinical and experimental aspects of hypnotic dreams, in Kline, M. V.: *Clinical Correlations of Experimental Hypnosis*. Springfield, Ill., Thomas, 1963.

∽∽Part Four∼∼∼∼∼∼∼∼∼∼∼∼∼∼∼∼∼∼∼∼

1. Varying Views of the Structure of a Hypnoanalysis

FOR SOME PATIENTS, as few as one or two hypnotic interviews may, under certain circumstances, be helpful in eliciting significant information, even with therapeutic effect. The limited aspects of such explorations should hardly serve to warrant classifying them as hypnoanalysis, regardless of techniques employed. Yet they are called this, as, for example, in the case of one author who described such patients under the headings of hypnoanalysis and narcoanalysis (1). A fifty-two year old man was mentioned in connection with his concern about impotence. During two hypnosis sessions that followed oral intake of sodium amytal, he linked his sexual concern with fear of financial insecurity. The aftermath was that this previously unmarried man proceeded to marry happily. His financial situation also improved. I should think that however helpful this therapeutic contact might have been, it did not really fall into the category of a hypnoanalysis.

Occasionally some therapists will rely heavily on one particular specialized technique during the conduct of many sessions involving hypnotic settings. Despite the availability of many possible therapeutic methods already described for hypnoanalytic work, it would be warranted to classify the treatment as hypnoanalysis even though there is special emphasis on one technique preferred by the doctor and suitable for the patient. Meares, for example, has described hypnography as a method in hypnoanalysis by which black and white painting is utilized as the means by which the patient reveals pertinent psychological material (2). The method is considered useful for patients who do not verbalize easily in hypnosis. At the same time, graphic representation of conflict data can be therapeutic beyond the effects of verbal expression of the same conflicts.

In one of his publications, Robert Lindner claimed that as a routine he was inducing posthypnotic amnesia after each instance of hypnotic recall or revivification (3). He said that if properly done, this procedure guarantees protection of the ego against "the onslaught of the repressed." Here again there is stress on personal preferences although the assertions are open to question. The fact is that, as intimated earlier, the number of patients suitable for hypnoanalytic work would become greatly limited because of the restrictions in the number of those capable of achieving post-hypnotic amnesias. The clinical judgment of the therapist is virtually eliminated as far as the desirability of inducing amnesias at certain points is concerned, if the procedure is routine and mandatory. There is an implication that posthypnotic amnesia is effectively induced according to the wish of the hypnotist. In fact, its success would be less dependent on technical maneuvers than on the psychological needs of the patient at that particular time. If there is great need for him to remember, the attempt to induce amnesia would fail. Finally, the adaptability of the ego in gauging its required protection is far greater than has been imagined heretofore. These controls lie more with the patient than with the therapist.

When Lindner made the claim referred to above, he had been describing a phase in the hypnoanalysis of a patient who had previously committed a murder. It seems his victim had been a substitute for his mother and this fact dawned on him in the course of treatment. It was believed, because of the upset that followed, that an amnesia should have been induced. Later awareness on the part of the hypnoanalyst that clinical judgment should have directed this step should not, in my opinion, have given way to the generalization regarding induction of posthypnotic amnesias in all situations as specified earlier.

It is possible that Lindner's views may have been influenced by the fact that a number of his patients were seen when they were imprisoned in penal institutions. The problems presented and the personality types among the patients may have accounted for the concern Lindner expressed, even though he makes a point of hypnoanalysis calling for patients with reasonably good ego strength. The type of situation mentioned for the patient last referred to, with the severity of the reaction that followed, may possibly be encountered more than elsewhere among certain types of psychopathic personalities for whom he evidently believed hypnoanalysis is indicated. I am inclined to believe that such patients would be accepted less frequently in less controlled private practice settings by most therapists, with the exception of those specially trained, experienced and interested in the problems of psychopaths (4).

Some therapists rely heavily on the view that what a patient reveals, in abreaction for example, and the manner in which he reveals it, is influenced considerably by the emotional tone of the hypnotic setting which the therapist himself helps to establish. Admittedly the issue is not always as simple and pat as the claim implies, but this conveys the general idea. Without specific reference to hypnoanalysis as it is being discussed now, but in relation to meaningful investigative and therapeutic hypnosis, it has been pointed out that harrowing war experiences may be described without much emotion, in a calm setting, with significant benefit (5). Conn reaffirms the change in the development of psychotherapy from a physician-centered to a patient-centered view (6). He stresses that the traditional attitude toward hypnotherapy as essentially involving a passive state for the patient, with physician-centered techniques, is passing. Allowing for variations and flexibility in therapeutic approach based on changing transference requirements, I should say that this holds true for hypnoanalysis as well. It is surely applicable also for modified approaches in the realm of hypnotherapy, with deviations being influenced by the analyst's conscious purposes based on his understandings of the dynamics involved in the patient's problems and on the patient's special needs.

In a paper by Klemperer on changes of the body image in hypnoanalysis, she stressed this special theme of body image as a point of interest and importance that is amenable to study in the hypnotic setting (7). Yet she seems to prefer limiting the concept of hypnoanalysis by emphasizing certain techniques or special states when noting that the term, hypnoanalysis, implies that the patient is in a state of regression, experiencing revivification, or utilizing visualizations which he then attempts to interpret. Many additional points which I believe should be taken into consideration when discussing hypnoanalysis have already been mentioned here.

In another paper, Klemperer made reference to some patients she had treated with good results (8). One had previously been hospitalized for a "mild schizophrenia." He had considerable anxiety which he tried to allay with alcohol consumption. Another patient obtained some relief from hand tremors that appeared when he was in public places. His problem involved features of conversion and anxiety hysteria. A third patient found relief from episodes of hysterical depression. A fourth improved in a few months after presenting difficulties with heart palpitations and fear of imminent death. Klemperer has the impression that patients who have been in psychotherapy elsewhere are usually more difficult to hypnotize. It has not been my experience that this is generally true. I concur in her opinion that it would be desirable for hypnoanalytic measures to be used more frequently than happens now for certain suitable patients during initial therapeutic experiences, rather than after long periods of ineffective or partially effective psychotherapy or analysis without hypnosis. I must reemphasize that the statement applies to selected patients. Occasionally some patients who had previously been treated without hypnosis, had in fact asked for it. In such cases, and when hypnotherapy or hypnoanalysis is sought on initial contact, the motivations must of course be evaluated as I have consistently implied.

Meares has discussed certain aspects of such motivations with succinct reference, for example, to the woman who seeks help not mainly for her symptoms, but to engage in a hypnotic relationship in which she yearns to be overpowered (9). He makes reference also to the masculine-aggressive woman who believes she will not actually enter a hypnotic state, thus demonstrating her own ability to resist what she regards as submitting to a man. Meares points up the countertransference issues too where therapists may seek opportunities in the hypnotic relationship to express controlling, even sadistic needs.

2. Elaboration of Psychoanalytic Observations

Sharp awareness of transference-countertransference issues can prove significant beyond general importance for the conduct of a hypnoanalysis. It can assist, along with other features of hypnoanalytic work, in opening up opportunities for substantiating, through the hypnoanalysis itself, psychoanalytic theories and concepts and elaborating observations noted during the development of psychoanalysis. One example involved my interest in a Medusa's head dream experienced by a patient during his childhood and related in his adult life when in hypnoanalysis (Schneck, 10). The relating of the dream was connected with verbalizations during a hypnosis session reflecting a homosexual transference. Enhanced recall is often linked intimately with the nature of the hypnotic transference at the time certain memories emerge. The verbalizations that preceded mention of the Medusa's head dream were as follows: "I feel an impatience for something. I was waiting for you to say something and how I'd react to whatever was said. I seem to be relating more and more to an object, the object being you. At first I had a feeling of wanting to liberate myself, breaking a barrier of some kind. Then there was something fleeting, someone I once knew, her face and how she spoke. Then I became more aware of my physical feelings—arms, hands and legs. I would see your face every one in a while. Once I saw a snake as I saw a few weeks ago in the zoo." Then there were fantasies of a tunnel, and fantasies and recollections of snakes that were active and passive. "I looked at it with fascinated repulsion." Reference may be made to the original report for further details, but it need only be said at this time that the data supplemented, with a clinical case report, observations that Freud had made forty years before (11, 12).

3. Hypnosis-rebirth and Hypnosis-death Themes with Anthropological Observations

I pointed out earlier that within the setting of a hypnoanalysis I have been able to show how some people equate the hypnotic relationship with a homosexual contact. This equation can merge with others, such as the interesting hypnosis-death identification. The hypnosis-death equation can in turn merge with the identification of hypnosis and rebirth (Schneck, 13). A patient entered the hypnotic state and felt himself going into a grave. The grave in this case was a body of water. The water was black, and the deeper he entered it, the deeper he felt himself to be involved in the hypnosis. It was a "watery grave." He had had this experience also in a previous hypnosis session without having mentioned it at that time. Then he had felt he was underground and tried to come up for air. He grunted and coughed. He saw himself in profile, in the grave, with a transparent effect. It was similar to his nocturnal water dreams. Being under water, trying to breathe, resulted in a "womb" association. He regarded the grave and water symbolism as equivalents. "The womb and trying to come out of it—birth. To emancipate myself." Many of this patient's problems were closely associated with his relationship with his mother. His self-destructive tendencies did not appear to imply a wish for destruction as an end in itself, but a fantasy of obliteration and starting anew. I think this was reflected in the fusion of the hypnosis-death and hypnosis-rebirth themes. Also, I have been able to show that these findings in clinical work with patients are corroborated by observations among certain primitive peoples (Schneck, 14). I am inclined to believe that these unconscious identifications are of considerable importance in the widespread belief about great beneficial effects of the hypnotic state and hypnotic methods involving simple authoritative suggestion.

Regarding the aforementioned primitive settings, I might add that in the identification of hypnosis and death, there are at times an "as if" comparison and on some occasions an "it is the same" identification. Both of these relationships are encountered among patients in present day clinical hypnoanalytic situations. Writing about totemism and the ritual of death and destruction, Frazer said that in many "savage tribes" young boys at puberty experience initiatory rites (38). In a common one there is the symbolic killing of the child and bringing him to life again. He interpreted the rites from the view of their implying extracting the child's soul in order to transfer it to his totem. He said this would naturally suppose killing the youth or at least throwing him "into a death-like trance, which the savage hardly distinguishes from death" (33).

Rose has offered descriptions of rites among Australian aborigines, and what he has to say appears to substantiate the observations of Frazer regarding trance states and death. Trance states in some areas are described as death. In others, the interpretation and description of events are those of trance experiences. In some areas, trance is called death or "being killed." The postulant is mourned for (34). Readers concerned with additional related findings about trance and primitive settings are referred to the writings of Ackerknecht (35), Benedict (36), and Sigerist (37). They are certainly pertinent so far as a grasp of the over-all history of hypnosis is concerned. The specific link between trance and death will be found too in the literary works of several writers mentioned earlier, in the paragraphs dealing with the historical antecedents of hypnoanalysis.

4. Hypnosis, Transference, and Transference Analysis

The issues discussed here are connected with theories of hypnosis, and my views on this score are taken up in this volume and elsewhere (Schneck, 15). The point to be made now is that I see transference involvements as only part of the total picture of hypnosis and its meaning. They do not constitute the core of its significance which seems to me to have a more fundamental biological root. But stress on transference implications has led to somewhat superficial views of hypnosis and hypnotic relationships. Some of my observations are substantiated by others although they do not necessarily have to accept my views on theory. Gill has mentioned the claim that the patient's ego regression and objectification of transference fantasies in the hypnotic relationship results in making the transference unanalyzable (16). He points out that subjects in deep hypnosis can examine the hypnotic state itself, with transference implications, including the induction process. This is surely true. I would add that a "deep" hypnosis in its classical sense is not even necessary.

An additional highlighted claim is that theoretically a successful analysis should result in disappearance of hypnotizability. Gill said this was not encountered, and the point is stressed that hypnosis may be grounded in very primitive transferences which are encouraged in the hypnotic setting. This may result in persistence of hypnotizability. I believe that the transference elements are important but that these interpersonal issues are secondary elements superimposed on the core of hypnosis which is basically and innately biological, a fundamental aspect of total psychophysiological functioning. It is for the latter reason that transference resolution has nothing to do with basic ability or inability to experience the hypnotic state. Transference involvements on the other hand may enhance or detract from the ability to enter hypnosis to some degree under certain circumstances. I feel that symptomatic change need not be undone even if the transference is evaluated with the patient. Gill noted that in his opinion there is no such thing as complete resolution of transference by analysis.

Some of the points taken up by Gill appeared also in another paper that he issued in collaboration with Menninger (17). It pertained to the hypnoanalysis of a thirty-six year old woman with symptomatology that included neurasthenic, hysterical, and depressive features. The patient was seen five times a week for one hundred and thirty-three interviews and achieved considerable symptomatic improvement. A point of interest lay in the issue of hypnotizability when intravenous sodium penetothal was used to deepen the hypnosis. Usually experienced hypnotherapists do not employ this measure although there are exceptions. It was noticed that many attempts to achieve improvement in hypnotizability through use of pentothal in other patients were uniformly unsuccessful. From what is known now about the complex psychological elements that are involved in hypnotizability and hypnotic behavior in general, these findings are understandable.

One of the techniques in the treatment setting just mentioned involved the use of hypnotic dreams. As has been intimated already, such measures are used frequently in hypnoanalytic work. As a result of the frequent effectiveness of dream induction during hypnosis, or the use of posthypnotic suggestions in hypnosis for subsequent nocturnal dreaming, I have transferred the technique at times to treatment settings that do not involve the use of hypnosis. Some patients can indeed produce and use nocturnal dreams by telling themselves in advance that they will dream, sometimes about a particular theme. Experimental work has been done in this area. Fisher claimed that patients in analysis may accept dream suggestions to a degree approaching that in hypnotic subjects (18). Not surprising is the fact that when suggestions are given, behavior resembles that of hypnotic subjects. It was felt that the state of induced regression inherent in hypnotic and analytic contacts entails increased suggestibility as one of its properties. The hypnotic relationship was viewed and discussed within the context of ego functioning and impulse-defense relationships. It was felt that there was nothing specific about the hypnotic state. Hypnotic phenomena appear as a result of interaction of psychic attitudes of the subject toward the physician and the activity of the doctor in this relationship involving induced regression. These views fall into the category of those aspects of hypnosis only partially involved in any attempt at explanation of the hypnotic state itself. These transference elements are present but are not crucial to the core of hypnosis as I view it in its theoretical aspects.

5. Spontaneous Hypnotic and Self-hypnotic States

The fact that some patients in analysis move spontaneously into hypnosis on certain occasions is apparent to anyone willing to see it, and with a sufficient measure of experience to recognize it. Fliess has discussed this happening as an hypnotic evasion which is a manifestation of resistance (19). He regards it as a method the patient uses to counteract mobilization of impulse, through paralysis. I agree on the importance of the transference as far as the stimulation of such reactions is concerned. I feel, however, that the happening can be of potential usefulness, beyond the confines of the non-hypnotic analytic setting if the analyst is equipped to employ hypnoanalytic procedures. If this cannot be done, he is limited to attempts to analyze the phenomenon and to deal with it accordingly. Difficulties on this score may arise. In connection with one of his cases, for example, this hypnotic evasion was evaluated but could not be abolished. It was concluded that the unconscious need for punishment could not be made conscious. The analysis was discontinued. I think it can be seen that the appearance of the hypnotic state under certain circumstances, as just described, ties in with observations that Fisher made regarding similarity of the behavior in analytic patients and hypnotic subjects when dream suggestions were offered.

The tendency for some patients in analysis to enter a hypnotic state spontaneously serves as a reminder of occurrences that are of a different type and important to note. Occasionally, one encounters patients with the tendency to have auto-hypnotic experiences, if not prior to treatment then during the course of it. Experience and good judgment determine decisions to accept such patients for hypnotherapy or hypnoanalysis, a fundamental issue being their inherent degree of ego strength. An example of an unfortunate happening is offered by one writer in the case of a forty year old woman said to have been treated hypnoanalytically each day, for one year, with one or two hours sessions (20). She had been hospitalized for a total amnesia. With productive explorations she became increasingly tense, confused, depressed, and preoccupied with suicidal thoughts. In removing the amnesia she was left with conflicts that could not be managed. The autohypnotic episodes ensued with self-destructive feelings and behavior. After electroconvulsive therapy was instituted, the total amnesia reappeared and the patient was more manageable. As with all other delicate psychotherapeutic measures, the case illustrates the importance of careful selection of patients, and painstaking work with regard for the nature of the patient's illness, the degree of ego strength, the role of the patient's defenses and how they are dealt with.

The point about autohypnosis brings up the issue of the advisability of having a patient use self-hypnosis in the course of a hypnoanalysis (Schneck, 21). Occasionally patients inquire about it. More rarely do they seriously consider it. The hypnoanalyst may regard it as of possible use in patients who are not too ill, but thus far among all who employ hypnoanalysis, the incorporation of self-hypnosis into the treatment of a patient is relatively infrequent. I have had patients use it occasionally. An important consideration for serious and effective work by the patient is ample time to use the self-hypnosis consistently. Patients who enter hypnosis rapidly after preliminary experience are often able to achieve self-hypnosis with ease. The fact that the usual resistances in treatment play a role in self-hypnosis too accounts in part for the fact that it is easy for a patient to lose interest in it rapidly or to supply a series of rationalizations for not having employed it as frequently as originally intended. In properly selected patients the abuse of the procedure, its use beyond the needs intended for treatment, and the issue of habituation, appears to present no serious problem. The idea of self-hypnosis is identified more readily with oriental cultures rather than occidental customs, and this in my opinion is one reason why it has not become part of routine therapeutic activity to the degree that heterohypnotic methods have come into use. In limited instances when self-hypnosis is employed, it may be found helpful not as a routine device introduced indiscriminately through the course of a hypno-analysis, but at certain points for additional exploration if it proves to be effective. Regarding the techniques employed during the self-hypnosis, free association and visual imagery methods have been relied on most frequently by my patients, with occasional exceptions. Part of the visual imagery methods include self-hypnotic dreams. They can be used in the same way as are dreams during hetero-hypnotic settings. They are treated in terms of associations and interpretations as are other hypnotic dreams and nocturnal dreams as well.

6. Self-hypnotic Dreams in Hypnoanalysis

The over-all study of self-hypnotic dreams includes their comparison in one individual with dreams by others. When self-hypnotic dreams are studied in terms of form and content, they should be compared with hetero-hypnotically induced dreams and nocturnal dreams of the same individual as I stated earlier. Frequently all such dreams are indistinguishable, not only in the patient's judgment, but by the hypnoanalyst, and by other professional workers who do not know in advance the settings in which the dreams occurred. I might note parenthetically that in a brief study of dual hypnotic dreams, findings pointed to the similarity or relatedness among them as in any series of spontaneous nocturnal dreams occurring during any one night (69). Links are encountered in the latent themes, if not in the manifest content. For a particular patient, a series of three dual hypnotic dreams was analyzed and relatedness discovered in latent content in each case. In one instance, relatedness in manifest content was observed. The subject was a patient in hypnoanalysis. The investigation took place in connection with evaluations of hypnosis as a research tool (Schneck, 70).

In self-hypnotic dreams well known dream mechanisms play a role, "classic" symbolism is observed, and repetitive use of certain symbols peculiar to the patient's individual functioning is encountered. Such dreams may be employed to extend and

intensify hypnoanalytic activity, involving the patient more completely in treatment. New issues are introduced, problems are
brought into sharp focus, resistances are further identified and
analyzed, transference concerns are clarified. In this way they
extend the purpose and role and use of hetero-hypnotic and
nocturnal dreams.

A twenty-nine year old patient had been considering the issue
of latent homosexuality, but avoided working satisfactorily on it.
She had a self-hypnotic dream. "I'm standing on a high cliff
which goes straight down to the sea. There are some jagged rocks
at the base. I'm debating as to whether I should jump or dive in.
(Here I'm wondering about suicide.) I stand at the very edge,
peer over and then straighten up. I do this several times. Then I
poise myself as for a dive. Just as I start to throw my weight
forward a young man grabs me from behind and stops me. I
say to him, 'What did you do that for?' He asks me what I was
trying to do. I tell him I wanted to take a dive. He tells me it's
dangerous to dive from here, as there are submerged rocks that
can't be seen from the top of the cliff. He says if I want to dive
there is a place nearby that is safe. We walk down a little way
and there is another cliff not so high. I can see people swimming
around at the base. I hesitate and he tells me there's nothing to
be afraid of. I ask him if he's going in and though he looks reluctant
he says he will. I ask him doesn't he like diving. He says not
particularly but he'll do it anyway and show me how. He calls
down, 'Look out below,' waits 'til the water is clear, then dives
in. I do the same. Then we swim along the rocks and I see a cave.
We swim in. It's moist, wet, and dripping from the ceiling and
is full of eerie light. I ask him where the light comes from. He says
from a big crack in the roof. I say, 'How can it? I didn't see any
crack in the ground above here.' He says, 'It's there if you know
where to look'. I suggest we go up to the hotel and ask how we
get there. He tells me to follow and I do. We swim over to a flight
of stairs and a platform rising up the cliffside. Then I notice there
is a chair lift. I ask him if he's coming on the lift with me and he
replies, 'No, this one you'll have to do yourself and alone.' I go
up and when I get to the top he tells me to wait for him. I reply,
'What for? You said I had to do it alone," and I start out. He

catches up to me and we walk to the hotel together and we get outside it. We say goodbye."

A partial evaluation of the dream revealed that she associated vagina to the crack (after some blocking) and referred to it as "not too appealing, and upsetting." Suicide pertained to thoughts she had had in the past. The chair lift gave rise to thoughts about eventually terminating treatment and the question as to whether she would need her analyst. The cliff events gave rise to associations about attempting to involve the doctor with herself in treatment, and "Trying to get you to do more of the work." This related to work on the theme of homosexuality. She was able to reveal that part of her problem was hesitancy in dealing with the issue for fear that she would discover herself to be homosexual, without normal sexual reactions. She believed the dream reflected her current belief that this was not necessarily so. "He says they are there if you look for them"—the crack in the roof. The very end of the dream may have reflected hostility toward her doctor for encouraging her to make her own efforts.

Self-hypnotic dreams may be used to explore the significance of symptoms and to clarify interpersonal relations. They certainly possess intrinsic interest as a mirror of personality functioning (Schneck, 22). In contrast to the more involved dream of the patient mentioned above, another patient with chronic anxiety reported the following: "Went into some kind of store to buy a blouse. Saw three lace cotton blouses. Wanted the one in front. The salesgirl said she didn't have that one." To this the patient associated, "I want things that I can't have." There was also a dream with clear transference implications. "A cracked glass rolling on the floor, I think. Someone suffering. Dr. S. I think." She associated herself to the glass and it was I who was suffering because of it. "In the dream your face looked sad. Suffering mentally. You would be unhappy if I weren't straightened out. Possibly my not working hard at these things (problems) was to make you unhappy."

Self-hypnotic dreams may also have the quality of nightmares. "Angelo was a conductor. Wouldn't let me on the train. The train was moving. Had a terrific struggle with him. Went back a few cars and climbed on. Started through the trains. Angelo standing with back towards me in the vestibule. Wanted to push him but didn't. Ran to the security of the next train. Felt greatly relieved."

7. The Concept of Hypnotic Scene Visualization

Some time ago I began to use the term "scene visualization" for visual imagery that depicted settings essentially representative of what one may encounter in every-day life. This would be distinguished from a hypnotic dream where more distortion and symbolic representation is evident along with the usual variety of dream mechanisms. There may be encountered imagery serving as a continuum between the two. In such imagery, the subjects or patients have their eyes closed. I have already mentioned that I prefer to use the term "visual hallucinations" when external stimuli, not actually present, are seen as being present when the subject or patient has his eyes open. The distinction is often ignored in various writings so that the reader, unless attuned to this issue, cannot know the real nature of the experience. The confusion was present in some of the writings by Cooper, and it was only in personal conversation with him that I learned his subjects often had their eyes closed although he referred to their experiences as hallucinatory (23, 24).

The visual imagery I described, and hallucinatory occurrences, are different orders of experience. On an obvious level of significance one may point out that many more patients can experience various forms of visual imagery than hallucinatory activity as just defined. Aside from implying that the experiences are dramatic, the lack of differentiation may be traced in part, perhaps, to frequent references to nocturnal dreams as hallucinatory, especially in psychoanalytic writings. Even hypnotic dreams are referred to in this way (25). If one intends to avoid the confusion, it can be done in the same way that simple hypnotic recall can be distinguished from episodes coming closer to hypnotic regression. The tendency to imply something more dramatic is probably indicative of exhibitionistic and omnipotent strivings encountered at times. Sometimes, especially in the less experienced investigators, it is probably an oversight. The self-hypnotic dreams mentioned above should fall into the larger category of visual imagery. The matter of hypnotic hallucinations should be explored more fully (Schneck, 26).

8. Hypnoanalysis and Hypnotic Hallucinations

In hypnotic visual hallucinations and in hypnotic auditory hallucinations the stimuli are usually discerned as external to the individual. A patient imagining sounds or conversation as an implied inner experience is not hallucinating. Yet patients may evaluate critically the nature of their hypnotic hallucinatory experiences without implying any change in the nature of the hallucinatory occurrence. To add to the complexity, negative visual hallucinations with avoidance reactions are apparently a different order of experience from such hallucinations that do not entail an avoidance reaction. Apparently little understood neuropsychological functioning on the level of cortical integration differs, in some way, in these experiences. These varieties of experience are obviously significant in studies of perception.

Hallucinatory experiences have played a lesser role in my work with many patients in hypnoanalysis than have other techniques. Fewer patients are capable of functioning this way, and one must be especially careful of poor ego functioning when patients are considered for these approaches. Occasionally some very interesting happenings unfold. A young man worked well with hallucinatory experiences during his hypnoanalysis. In certain sessions he was able to converse with the hallucinated images of his mother and father. He hallucinated on visual and auditory levels. In his conversations he endeavored to ascertain his parents' attitudes about certain problems that concerned him. As the conversations progressed he learned that his mother's views on some issues were not quite what he had previously believed them to be. This troubled him. Later, following the hypnotic discussions, he spoke of the visual hallucinations but said the comments made by his mother were not external stimuli perceived by him. Rather, they were constructs of his own thinking at the time. This seemed to be a point of interest, but what he said was not questioned. Afterwards, to reevaluate the events, it was arranged for him to relive the hypnotic sessions. He became aware of the fact that he was indeed having auditory hallucinations, and the comments by his parents were in Yiddish while he was speaking in English. When these happenings were reviewed with the patient, he revealed that he had been reluctant to accept the implications of his mother's beliefs and feelings as they emerged during the hypnotic conversations. He isolated the significance of the issues from the mainstream of his personality functioning, validating the visual phenomena and denying the hallucinatory aspect of the auditory phenomena. On a waking level, following the original hypnosis sessions, he recalled the events incorrectly. The method by which this phase of the analysis was handled resulted in piercing the barriers of isolation and rationalization so essential for him at the time, yet obviously amenable to reduction and evaluation. These circumstances highlight in general the difficulty involved in evaluating all material elicited in treatment settings, hypnotic or non-hypnotic. More specifically they show how personality problems and strivings influence hypnotic behavior, and how it is possible for them to be judged or misjudged by patient and therapist alike.

It should be pointed out that some patients may indeed have hallucinatory experiences on one level and not on another. For example, a young woman held similar conversations with her parents during the course of hypnoanalytic work. She was able to experience auditory hallucinations involving their comments to her, while able to visualize them only on the imagery level, as described earlier, with her eyes closed. The dynamic importance of one level of experience as opposed to another varies with patients and in the same patient from time to time. The ability to have hallucinatory experiences, as described, may have greater emotional impact for some patients at certain times, but there is no direct relationship necessarily existing between ability to achieve this and the likelihood of greater therapeutic gain. Each case must be evaluated separately.

9. The Concept of Defensive Productivity in Relation to Hypnosis

One may wonder about reactions of patients after they have experienced one or more productive hypnotic sessions in terms of ready acceptance of continued use of hypnosis or resistance to it if hypnotic disclosures have generated anxiety. Needless to say, the reactions of patients vary considerably. As implied, however, some may temporarily maneuver sessions in a way that postpones reintroduction of hypnotic techniques. Patients may be relatively resistant and unproductive for awhile, or they may in fact be productive without recourse to hypnotic settings. It is as if they effect a compromise, permitting productivity on a consciously or unconsciously selective basis, while deferring productivity involving the analyst as a more active, guiding force. This is related also to situations in which hypnosis has been considered but not as yet initiated. The threat implied in its use results for some patients in procrastinating tactics, while as a compromise their productivity increases or their symptoms ease.

One may observe this frequently. Ellis (27) made a point of it and offered case illustrations. He cited one example of a forty year old single woman with an irresistable urge to look at the genital region of almost every man she met, with concurrent distress because she was certain that this was observed by others. By various maneuvers of postponement or avoidance she kept deferring the use of hypnosis for further exploration or symptom amelioration. Her urges and anxieties would ease. This pattern would be repeated from time to time.

Another woman, twenty-two years old, was rather unproductive for many sessions. She verbalized more freely and meaningfully only when the use of hypnosis was suggested. The pattern was observed again thereafter with a period of inhibition followed by release in an apparent reaction to suggestions that hypnosis be used. Ellis cites also the case of a thirty-five year old man who could not remember details of his life before the age of twelve. Hypnosis was suggested but the patient arrived late for his session, seemed relieved that hypnotic induction would not then take place, and revealed the recapture of some early memories prior to the twelve year age level. Examples of such functioning may be found in the records of many experienced hypnotherapists.

In contrast to what I might call this "defensive productivity" as a response to a therapist's suggesting the use of hypnosis, patients may indeed be productive in the sense of furnishing material through the use of hypnotherapy initiated at their own request The material furnished varies in character and may even include the recapture of buried memories. In the absence of good potential for personality integration, failure is encountered eventually in many of these cases. Moss (28) reported details of a thirty-one year old woman suffering from feelings of unreality, seizures, frigidity, and an "embryo dual personality." She requested hypnotherapy following several non-hypnotic individual psychotherapy sessions with another therapist. During the course of hypnotic explorations, forgotten memories were revived and the apparent presence of a second personality was investigated. Despite the elicitation of seemingly rich and meaningful data, the treatment was seen finally to have been a failure.

10 Multiple Personalities

The point of an embryo dual personality brings up the issue of multiple personalities that played an interesting role in the history of hypnosis and psychopathology. For a time it seemed that they were being discovered no longer, but more recently the multiple personality theme has again appeared in print. The point is raised frequently that secondary personalities may be artifacts evoked in the course of hypnotic explorations. I have been especially conscious of this possibility during hypnoanalytic work but cannot supply a definite statement in support of this view even though dramatic examples of multiple personalities have not come my way in the years of constant exposure to psychologically ill patients. Some of the descriptions of secondary personalities show awareness of this issue by the therapists involved. They are evidently intent on avoiding the mistake of helping to construct the personality configurations that were believed by others to have emerged quite spontaneously.

Moss was aware of this potential pitfall and commented on it (28). In an earlier paper, Bowers and Brecher (29) took it into consideration. Moss made a point of saying that when the patient stopped mentioning the secondary personality, the issue was avoided thereafter by the therapist. It appeared desirable to adopt this course in treatment. I took the same course of action with a patient in hypnoanalysis and as a result some potentially fascinating aspects of psychopathology may have been by-passed in favor of treatment directions deemed more desirable for the patient. Needless to say, this is not always called for. Readers may obtain without difficulty other reports of recent years dealing with secondary personalities (30, 31, 39).

The publication by Sutcliffe and Jones (32) surveyed the multiple personality concept critically in its historical development and presented many interesting illustrations. The discussion touched on the conception of multiple personality as a diagnostic fashion, a product of shaping in therapy, an outgrowth of hypnotic suggestion, an example of simulation, and a personality picture consisting of extensions of characteristics of normal personalities. Significant alterations of the personality syndrome included loss of self-reference memories. There were confusions and delusions centering around identity in time and place. An hypnothesis discussed was that of parallels in multiple personality and hypnotic phenomena suggesting degrees of proneness to multiple personality as predictive of degrees of hypnotizability.

When reporting on her patient, Bowers mentioned that multiple personalities in classic form are associated with fugue states and total or partial amesias. She believed the fugue states were not always necessary, as in her patient, and in line with earlier comments here she mentioned that she believed the patient's multiple personality structure preceded the start of work with hypnosis so that it was not an artifact. Moss presented the case data as a study in hysteria. Bowers described a severely obsessive-compulsive personality with the suggestion that the obsessive-compulsive defense binds the underlying multiple personalities resulting in a rigid, cold, conflicted conscious personality. This contrasts with hysterical dissociation producing several personalities living out their roles in turn.

11. Behavior, Expectation, and Artifact

The point about the role the therapist might play in creating an apparent secondary personality that would be essentially an artifact applies to other aspects of hypnosis. Questions have been asked as to whether hypnosis itself is an artifact. In recent years there has been special concentration of attention, in this connection, on hypnotic regression and its validity. Various points about regression have already been taken up. In line with differences of opinion regarding the view to be taken of it, additional remarks are indicated. One must certainly allow for differences of opinion in such complex affairs. It is important to recognize the presence of shades and degrees of behavioral change. In dealing with regression, for example, Conn (33) said that the patient does not revive old memories. He deals with "memory romances" that are rationalizations and wish fulfilling fantasies. In some cases I should say this is quite true. In others it is probably far from true. But in line with shades of difference and with differences of opinion I might add that I have already pointed out the type of regression where the patient feels the situation to be more real than the original occurrence. This can probably be accounted for by the fusion of the basic experience with current transference identifications which in turn results in the greater feeling of reality. Even if the issue of this feeling of reality were not involved, many hypnotically regressed states may be strongly saturated with the impact of concurrent transference forces. But the core of the patient's personality and autonomous functioning, features of which are simply set in motion by the hypnotic setting and by hypnotic suggestions, must be recognized and accepted.

It would be a serious mistake to believe that the hypnotic subject feels and behaves only as he believes the hypnotherapist wishes of him. To the extent that this may be true in certain cases, the same would apply to therapeutic encounters in which hypnosis is not used at all. Treatment settings are always structured to lesser or greater degree and patients are always influenced to a point by what they believe is expected of them.

A patient sought hypnoanalysis after spending five years in conventional psychoanalysis. She exhibited, during initial contacts, childish, pouting, petulant behavior seemingly often so inappropriate that it suggested schizophrenic-like behavior. When this was called to her attention she said that her previous analyst had encouraged her to act as she felt. As she continued to behave in this way, she was of the impression that the analyst actually expected it of her. When the need for it was now questioned, her demeanor changed, and she revealed herself to be far more mature in fact than her earlier behavior had suggested.

References

1. London, L. S : Hypnosis, hypno-analysis and narco-analysis. *Amer. J. Psychother.*, *1:*443, 1947.

2. Meares, A.: Hypnography—a technique in hypnoanalysis. *J. Ment. Sci.*, *100:*965, 1954.

3. Lindner, R. M.: An evaluation of hypnoanalysis, in *Current Therapies of Personality Disorder*. New York, Grune and Stratton, 1946.

4. Lindner, R. M., and Seliger, R. V.: The hypnoanalytic technique with prisoners, in *Handbook of Correctional Psychology*. New York, Philosophical Library, 1947.

5. Conn, J. H.: Hypnosynthesis, 3. Hypnotherapy of chronic war neuroses with a discussion of the value of abreaction, regression, and revivification. *J. Clin. Exp. Hyp.*, *1:*29, 1953.

6. Conn, J. H.: Hypnotic relaxation and analysis, in *Therapy Through Hypnosis*. New York, Citadel Press, 1952.

7. Klemperer, E.: Changes of the body image in hypnoanalysis. *J. Clin. Exp. Hyp.*, *2:*157, 1954.

8. Klemperer, E.: Hypnosis and hypnoanalysis. *J. Amer. Med. Wom. Ass.*, *8:*164, 1953.

9. Meares, A.: Some moral and ethical aspects of medical hypnosis. *Practitioner*, *183:*329, 1959.

10. Schneck, J. M.: A hypnoanalytic note on a Medusa's Head dream. *J. Nerv. Ment. Dis.*, *131:*80, 1960.

11. Freud, S.: The infantile genital organization of the libido, a supplement to the theory of sexuality (1923), in *Collected Papers*. London, Hogarth Press, 1946, vol. 2.

12. Freud, S.: Medusa's Head (1922), in *Collected Papers*. London, Hogarth Press, 1950, vol. 5.

13. Schneck, J. M.: Hypnosis-death and hypnosis-rebirth concepts in relation to hypnosis theory. *J. Clin. Exp. Hyp.*, *3:*40, 1955.

14. Schneck, J. M.: The hypnotic trance, magico-religious medicine, and primitive initiation rites. *Psychoanal. Rev.*, *41:*182, 1954.

15. Schneck, J. M.: A theory of hypnosis. *J. Clin. Exp. Hyp.*, *1:*16, 1953.

16. Gill, M. M.: Ego psychology and psychotherapy. *Psychoanal. Quart.*, *20:* 62, 1951.

17. Gill, M. M., and Menninger, K.: Techniques of hypnoanalysis illustrated in a case report. *Bull. Menninger Clin.*, *10:*110, 1946.

18. Fisher, C.: Studies on the nature of suggestion. Part 1: experimental induction of dreams by direct suggestion. *J. Amer. Psychoanal. Ass.*, *1:* 222, 1953.

19. Fliess, R.: The hypnotic evasion: a clinical observation. *Psychoanal. Quart.*, *22:*497, 1953.
20. Barahal, H. S.: Hypnosis in medicine. *New York J. Med.*, *59:*1552, 1959.
21. Schneck, J. M.: Self-hypnotic dreams in hypnoanalysis. *J. Clin. Exp. Hyp.*, *1:*44, 1953.
22. Schneck, J. M.: The therapeutic use of self-hypnotic dreams. *J. Clin. Exp. Hyp.*, *1:*28, 1953.
23. Cooper, L. F.: Time distortion in hypnosis. *Bull. Georgetown Univ. Med. Cent.*, *1:*214, 1948.
24. Cooper, L. F., and Erickson, M. H.: Time distortion in hypnosis. 2. *Bull. Georgetown Univ. Med. Cent.*, *4:*50, 1950.
25. Mazer, M.: An experimental study of the hypnotic dream. *Psychiatry*, *14:*265, 1951.
26. Schneck, J. M.: Hypnotic hallucinatory behavior. *J. Clin. Exp. Hyp.*, *1:*4, 1953.
27. Ellis, A.: Reactions of psychotherapy patients who resist hypnosis. *J. Clin. Exp. Hyp.*, *1:*12, 1953.
28. Moss, C. S., Thompson, M. M., and Nolte, J.: An additional study in hysteria: the case of Alice M. *Int. J. Clin. Exp. Hyp.*, *10:*59, 1962.
29. Bowers, M. K., and Brecher, S.: The emergence of multiple personalities in the course of hypnotic investigation. *J. Clin. Exp. Hyp.*, *3:*188, 1955.
30. Erickson, M. H., and Kubie, L. S.: The permanent relief of an obsessional phobia by means of communications with an unsuspected dual personality. *Psychoanal. Quart.*, *8:*471, 1939.
31. Thigpen, C. H., and Cleckley, H.: A case of multiple personality. *J. Abnorm. Soc. Psychol.*, *49:*135, 1954.
32. Sutcliffe, J. P., and Jones, J.: Personal identity, multiple personality, and hypnosis. *Int. J. Clin. Exp. Hyp.*, *10:* 231, 1962.
33. Conn, J. H.: Meanings and motivations associated with spontaneous hypnotic regression. *J. Clin. Exp. Hyp.*, *6:*21, 1958.
34. Rose, R.: Psi and Australian aboriginals. *J. Amer. Soc. Psychical Res.*, *46:*17, 1952.
35. Ackerknecht, E. H.: "Mesmerism" in primitive societies. *Ciba Symposia*, *9:*826, 1948.
36. Benedict, R.: *Patterns of Culture*. New York, Penguin, 1947.
37. Sigerist, H. E.: *A History of Medicine*. Vol. 1, Primitive and Archaic Medicine. New York, Oxford University Press, 1951.
38. Frazer, J. G.: *The Golden Bough*. New York, Macmillan, 1945.
39. Morton, J. H., and Thoma, E.: A case of multiple personality. *Amer. J. Clin. Hyp.*, *6:*216, 1964.

∽Part Five∽∽∽∽∽∽∽∽∽∽∽∽∽∽∽∽∽∽∽∽

1. Confirmation of Psychoanalytic Observaions

As ONE REVIEWS the writings on hypnoanalysis, it is evident that at least some investigators have been caught up in the attraction to past memories, their influence, and abreaction, to the exclusion of broader concerns in psychoanalytic work. Yet for some time a few have indeed been interested in a wider range of activity, not only with the view of confirming and overlapping with hypnotic measures those tenets accepted by other psychoanalytic therapists but with the wish to add new observations and perspectives whenever possible. At times these efforts have met with success.

Robert Lindner (1) reported on a patient with hysterical somnambulism. He was concerned with clarifying further the mechanisms of hysteria and its expression in the form of somnambulism. At the same time he was interested in presenting his techniques based on five years of experience with inmates of a federal penitentiary. Points involved in his approach were discussed earler in this book. Here again, there is concentration of attention on bringing repressed material to the surface, and Lindner combined, in his treatment, periods of hypnosis and free association. He wanted "to validate beyond doubt the substrata of awareness, and to imbed firmly as novel accretions to the personality the analytic interpretations and significances arrived at by the patients own efforts."

The patient was seen one hour each day, six days a week, for three months. It was shown that his difficulties incorporated latent homosexuality, sadism, and castration anxiety. Lindner concluded that the symptom of somnambulism served as a protective device for the ego to escape id urges and the demands of a primitive superego. It permitted avoidance of guilt, and freedom from it. As in other writings issued by him, Lindner stressed abreactive advantages through hypnosis, and hypnoanalysis as a time-saving measure.

Alcoholics are known to be difficult to treat with good results, regardless of methods employed. It would be hard to say whether hypnotherapy offers much more promise than other methods but efforts are made by those especially interested in the problem and from time to time reports are issued (2). Some papers stress special features within a total treatment situation and one such is that of Wolberg who described the relief of a hand anesthesia in a forty-two year old alcoholic with a history of repeated hospitalizations (3). In recounting the hypnoanalysis, a number of references are given to dream material, but the final break-through occurred with the technique of having the patient look into a mirror placed on a table next to which he was seated. He was in hypnosis at the time. After orientation to a four to six year age level he was instructed to observe the scene appearing in the mirror. He reacted with strong emotion to the evoked recollection dealing with masturbation, its discovery, and associated parental threats. What he saw in the mirror was himself with four fingers missing from his right hand. The recollection of intimidation by his father followed this scene. The patient experienced anxiety when discussing the issue afterwards, but presumably he was able to cope with it satisfactorily. The anesthesia disappeared and was said not to have recurred during a three year period of additional contact with the patient.

The above-mentioned report focussed largely on the one symptom of hand anesthesia. The same author supplied a more involved account of the hypnoanalysis of a schizophrenic (4). Another long account of a patient was prepared by Freytag. Her patient had been a drug addict and had already been in psychoanalytic therapy for three hours each week over a period of one and a half years. Among persistent symptoms was a troublesome agoraphobia (5).

A lengthy case report was included by Watkins (6) in a larger work dealing with military service cases. It was described as the hypnoanalytic treatment of an entrenched phobia, and the patient presented as his complaint the "feeling that somebody was out to get me." One form it assumed was the fear of going to bed at night unless the light was left on in his room. The relief for this patient was achieved in two steps according to the author. He says that the fear lessened first, and phobia of the dark was replaced by anxiety dreams after the patient saw his fear as related to projection of personal guilt feelings. These dreams then disappeared when he worked through oedipal feelings toward his mother, with disclosure of his latent homosexuality or fears of passivity. Caution is expressed in connection with likely long term persistence of favorable results. This is worth noting because of the prevalence of dogmatic optimism in many cases, stated or implied in reports on hypnotherapy and in psychoanalytic literature. Rarely is it noted that patients presumably helped significantly turn up later in the offices of other therapists. This holds true for any type of treatment, including especially both short and long periods of psychoanalysis.

2. The Nature of Hidden Determinants in Deceptive Requests for Hypnoanalysis

The point just mentioned is significant in relation to what I have had occasion to note as hidden determinants in deceptive requests for hypnoanalysis (Schneck, 7). We know that patients have many unconscious fantasies about the hypnotic state and hypnotic relationships. We know too that these fantasies have an important bearing on requests for hypnoanalysis. They involve dependency longings, sexual strivings and omnipotence wishes. They incorporate also masochistic tendencies and desires for symbolic death and rebirth experiences. There are other items that play a role in the requests for hypnoanalysis, items that often are not recognized by therapists despite their importance. And they are important in their bearing on decisions regarding the initiation and management of treatment. Frequently their evaluation indicates that patients seeking hypnoanalysis do not, in fact, really wish to have treatment incorporate hypnotic techniques. In this respect the requests are deceptive. When this point is evaluated with patients at the proper time, many can view the issues more realistically and consider carefully the possible desirability of delaying introduction of hypnotic techniques pending assessment of indications and contraindications, the desirability of relinquishing hypnoanalysis completely, or in fact embarking on it with a better view of its real significance for them. Elicitation of hidden determinants and bringing them to awareness from previous unconscious or preconscious positions broadens insights into ego-psychological operations within the analytic contacts. It contributes to greater understanding of the broad spectrum of personality functioning.

It must be evident that to initiate hypnoanalysis when a patient really does not wish it can complicate treatment and create confusion. The patient deceives the hypnoanalyst. He is faced with feelings of guilt that interfere with various aspects of treatment efforts. To some degree his respect for the analyst is impaired by the success in his deception. If the hypnoanalyst recognizes the maneuver, better understandings are made impossible. Confidence and respect may be restored. The decision may then be made to continue with the use of hypnosis based on more complete recognition of needs for it, abandon it as unnecessary or ill-advised, defer it, postpone all treatment, or introduce other recommendations.

Many patients seek hypnoanalysis with little idea of its real merits and possibilities. They are influenced by what they have read or heard in connection with its experimental features and "unorthodox" impressions. In effect, this carries an implied corollary that after preliminary inquiry or sampling, such treatment may be rejected. At some point it is important to clarify this ambivalence. Often such patients relinquish concern with hypnoanalysis and function well in treatment without use of hypnosis. Also, patients may resume hypnotic techniques following a phase of treatment without them, but with a more realistic approach. This change would occur in relation to significant issues inherent in the patients' problems and with meaningful timing. Occasionally, with clarification of unwarranted choice of hypnoanalysis, some patients may discontinue treatment completely. In such cases, they are generally poorly motivated to begin with. In any event, all patients in the categories just mentioned are essentially evaluating the issue of psychotherapy in general rather than hypnoanalysis specifically.

The hypnoanalyst sees patients who have been in treatment before, but who have discontinued. They may have had one or more treatment encounters elsewhere. As backgrounds are discussed, it becomes evident that they have terminated at points of intensified resistance. They may or may not have realized this at the time. Such issues must be looked into sooner or later. The seeking of hypnoanalysis probably served as a way out of previous therapeutic difficulties. After such evaluation, some patients may decide to return to previous analysts, especially when the break had been recent. At other times the patients may decide to continue, either on the basis of fantasies about hypnosis, or on the basis of realistic appraisals of hypnoanalysis, or in the belief that they may fare better in the new relationship whether or not hypnotic methods are employed. At least they understand more clearly the motivations for seeking hypnoanalysis. Indications for the latter should be appropriate if it is indeed to be the treatment of choice now.

The resistance theme has its counterpart in negative transference during phases of which some patients will terminate treatment and seek hypnoanalysis as a rationalization for changing doctors. What has been said in connection with the previous category of patients essentially applies here. Most patients who can see the significance of proper evaluation of their steps and their motivations tend to have a healthier regard for the hypnoanalyst whether or not they decide to continue with him, return to previous therapists, continue in treatment without hypnosis, or move into a hypnoanalytic relationship.

Similar occurrences involve patients who have achieved no gains in previous analytic contacts. They hesitate to terminate decisively owing to feelings of guilt bound up with the transference relationships. There must be a good reason to change doctors, and the decision based on special possibilities inherent in hypnoanalysis furnishes them with a valid excuse. In fact, it is the change itself that is important for them rather than a keen, realistic view of hypnoanalysis. Again, proper evaluation of these issues is important and decisions regarding further treatment, hypnoanalysis specifically, must be geared to meaningful motivation, aptitude, and therapeutic indications.

Allied to patients who claim they have previously made no progress, are those who admit achieving gains, but too few and too slowly. They insist they want results more rapidly and are attracted to a form of treatment offering this possibility in fact, but also with a background of often exaggerated publicity to this effect. What has been said of other patient groups applied here too, and at some point appropriate discussions are called for with good timing and within the framework of experienced clinical judgment. If such patients are capable of assessing merits and expectations in realistic perspective, they may become suitable candidates for hypnoanalysis.

If not, other forms of treatment may be indicated, assuming there is sincere willingness to pursue measures for additional help.

Not infrequently patients seek hypnoanalysis under the guidance or pressure of friends or relatives taken by it on the basis of hearsay claims. The patients themselves may not really want it, but they comply as far as initiating contact is concerned. Again, the hypnoanalyst must be able to discern the forces at play in order to insure cooperation of the patients in a true sense and to help them to see what they are really striving for as far as treatment in general in concerned. If this is not done in all cases comprising the general groups discussed above, both patient and therapist are operating blindly and cannot merge efforts to a reasonable degree in seeking appropriate goals. Resistances, transference operations and counter-transference reactions are all influenced as a result, to the detriment of the treatment situation itself, and with increased difficulties for patient and hypnoanalyst alike.

Should we consider again the issue of total time required for hypnoanalytic treatment, it is evident that the points just mentioned share in the outcome. The problems inherent in the situations that have been described must be resolved if treatment is to progress reasonably smoothly and without undue delays. I have stressed the proper discussion and assessment of these potential barriers, yet it is conceivable and it does happen that these important potential ob-obstacles are resolved in short order, early in treatment, without verbalization, by virtue of a rapidly unfolding positive transference that in itself dissolves the barriers carried into the initial contact. I believe these barriers generally are recognized in time and are brought to the surface.

3. Hypnotic Imagery and Second Selves

In the effort to deal with underlying issues of importance in symptom formation or characterological problems, and to cope with resistance and transference concerns, measures are introduced from time to time that constitute variations of more standard hypnotic techniques, or that amount to stress on special aspects of hypnotic behavior evoked by such techniques. Sometimes the special point is not so much a different type of production during the hypnosis, but an area of emphasis injected into it. The interpretation I am placing on such events holds true, I believe, in Klemperer's presentation, for example, of material dealing with childhood fantasies or experiences brought to the fore in hypnotic regression. She centers attention on the tendency of some patients to appear to watch such events from a distance while they are taking place. She says the "watcher" phenomenon may occur spontaneously or be elicited by questions such as inquiring about the identity of the watcher. The projected personalities vary in age levels from time to time. Usually the watcher is at an age level beyond that of the child depicted in the main visualization (8).

In her writings and technical procedures, Klemperer appears to place heavy emphasis on regression. In line with this, another paper places stress on primary object-relationships revealed in hypnoanalysis (9). She was dealing firstly with the concern as to whether claims of patients in hypnotic regression are true recollections or fantasy material. She thought it might be helpful to examine spontaneous statements of patients regressed in hypnoanalysis for comparison with material obtained from patients in psychoanalysis. Then it would be determined whether information that is obtained fits the theories derived from psychoanalytic observations. This, at least, was the premise she brought to the clinical setting. The approach is reminiscent of some of Lindner's interests in his work with hypnosis. Elsewhere, Klemperer explored social anxiety, and early sexual and aggression theories as revealed through hypnoanalysis (11).

A second point of emphasis in Klemperer's writings is on time required for treatment, a theme that has also been discussed earlier in this volume. Within this context she talked about symbols and their interpretation, pointing out the stress on free association technique in conventional psychoanalytic settings. In comparison to free association leading to determination of the significance of a symbol, she mentions the technique of a visualization changing to its unconscious representation in the form of another visual image. The manipulation of images during hypnoanalysis, in an attempt to fathom their unconscious representations, is a device that can be used often with many patients, I should say. In the article by Klemperer, she plays up the point of one picture being worth a thousand words and states, "The highest form of verbalization strives toward the presentation of the image again—as in poetry" (10).

Hypnoanalytic measures have been used often to explore the significance of illness in its role as a neurotic defense for maintenance of psychic equilibrium. Lerner discussed various secondary gains and presented a hypnoanalytic session involving an obsessive-compulsive patient who suffered a relapse as a defense against her fear of loss of her physician (12). Lerner (13) presented also the case of a thirty year old man with an "hallucinatory psychosis." He suffered "absences" and dual personality states of which the unconscious backgrounds were studied hypnoanalytically. The pathology was traced to childhood, with efforts by the patient at detachment and the creation of a more acceptable personal world. During "absences" the patient hallucinated his own body as a second self that represented his "bad side." Another hallucination represented his father in the form of an old man with a beard, forcing him to engage in "abnormal acts" that were afterwards forgotten. Lerner states that symptomatology disappeared as a result of the hypnoanalysis, without relapse during a year of subsequent observation.

The representation of a second self is described in writings by others. One of my patients in hypnoanalysis, a man in his twenties, visualized a figure he called "Little Me" during a series of sessions. This visualized individual was a small version of the patient that he associated with a younger age level although it was not a definite representation of himself as a child. This figure was critical of the patient and would sarcastically comment on his ideas and wishes, almost with impish delight. He would mock the patient's moral standards and appeared to be a carry-over of impulse trends from an earlier age period, trends largely held in check now but striving again for expresssion.

Another patient, a woman in her twenties, visualized on many occasions during hypnotic settings another self, more attractive, more free in self-expression, less moral, critical of the patient's activities and controls, more impulsive, indeed encouraging the patient to break away from more rigidly adhered to moral standards. She would engage the patient in a verbal exchange, supporting her own views, criticizing sharply, and with sarcasm. These visual representations lean heavily on concerns of superego functioning and probably constitute more clearly delineated personality constructs present in many people although generally more consistently buried and integrated within the total personality. In more sharply divided structures, the selves depicted here begin to assume a times rather separately functioning patterns leading in the direction of, or actually assuming characteristics that have been designated dual personalities, and in some cases multiple personalities.

4. Appearances and Behavior in Hypnoanalysis

In many hypnoanalytic settings, an observer other than the hypnoanalyst would see little unusual about the patient in terms of general behavioral features and verbal communication. Except for fine points in content of verbalization meaningful to the hypnoanalyst, the general tone of the utterances may not seem different on the surface from his comments when the hypnotic setting is not utilized. For other patients, however, differences are present although not the dramatic differences I have commented on elsewhere. The differences are in varying nuances of tone, timing, and choice of words. Patients, to put it one way, say things differently, and the manner in which they do so would be hard to predict. With every new encounter, I am curious as to how each patient will conduct himself. Frequently there are surprises in store. Though much is made of the influence of the manner of the hypnotist on the behavior elicited from subject or patient, a consideration that applies often of course, there are many occasions when careful scrutiny of one's possible influence fails to account satisfactorily for the manner in which the patient reveals his part of the hypnoanalytic situation.

An alcoholic patient, in hypnoanalysis, said the following, in fact and then in substance on certain occasions: "I'm just discouraged. There has to be hope. And as of now there's very little hope. I know I'm destroying myself. My father committed suicide. I've always said I wouldn't walk out on my kids as he did. Financially they'd be all right. But I want more out of life. I think I've devoted too much time to my kids . . . There doesn't seem to be too much hope. I'd like to think there is. I'd like to find hope. Yet I can't. I think the answer is to separate from A—(his wife) and to start to build a new life. I think that's the only way to keep going. A—is bad for me. She knows my condition and regardless of anything she'll gradually seduce me again."

During the same general time period, the patient in his ordinary state would deal essentially with the same factual content as in hypnosis. In hypnosis his speech would be slower than otherwise. It would often become a mere whisper. There would be long pauses. He would be much more self-absorbed. He would sound more pessimistic. He would give the impression of talking more to himself than to the hypnoanalyst. The depressive features would come more to the fore. He would dwell on feelings to a greater extent than on factual details of his everyday experience. These are some of the features that would be discerned fairly consistently.

Needless to say, it is not fundamentally important from the view of therapeutic progress whether a patient verbalizes freely or not during hypnosis provided that whatever verbalizations appear or whatever general behavior is elicited can be utilized constructively. Failing this, non-verbal communications may be helpful, such as drawing techniques and perhaps, if further investigations prove significant, techniques such as sensory hypnoplasty reported by Raginsky (26) but with which I have had no personal experience. With this measure, he says the hypnotized patient models clay to which various sensory stimuli have been added. They "stimulate basic primitive memories, associations, sensations and conflicts. The patient expresses repressed and suppressed material and then verbalizes his conflicts." Raginsky believes the therapeutic process is thereby initiated quickly and is much intensified. He stresses rapidity of recovery. He tells of the therapist remaining passive and silent throughout sessions.

The passivity of the analyst or hypnoanalyst often alluded to is, in my opinion and one in which others undoubtedly share, a considerably active role of a special type. It is, in effect, not talking and with meaning. Its stress by Raginsky in relation to the hypnoplasty technique is in sharp contrast to active verbal exchange illustrated, for example, in a patient with impotence reported a few years ago by Watkins (27). In both reports, however, there is focus of attention on rapidity of therapeutic change. What must be emphasized now is the fact that seemingly rapid change must often be held in check with patients. Meaningful changes can be tolerated in degrees, a point often but not invariably recognized. Patients may be overwhelmed by "insights" or by too many doors opening at the same time. The anxiety engendered in this way may retard rather than promote progress. Sometimes it leads to premature termination of treatment contacts. It has seemed to me that frequently the patient is caught in a trap of opposing wishes and capabilities. There is his desire to get well rapidly, and his inability really to improve as rapidly as he insists he should. Regardless of what help any therapist attempts to offer, the outcome may be unsatisfactory as far as the patient is concerned and he departs to seek other measures not long after treatment is initiated. For some it becomes an endless search.

The wish for being different, and becoming so very rapidly, takes on the coloring at times of rebirth experience. When changes are dramatic, it may be alluded to in this way and in such terms by the patient himself. At other times it may be implied. Treatment in general may be viewed as a rebirth experience. Hypnosis specifically may be associated with rebirth. It has some relation to the hypnosis-death concept that I have discussed elsewhere, moving into hypnosis implying moving into a state of death, and moving out of hypnosis implying rebirth. On some levels the details of which remain to be clarified, this issue seems to be connected with the phylogenetic theory of hypnosis that I have proposed. It is in terms of the phylogenetic regression being applicable to forms of lower life as well, with the hypnotic core related to the earliest differentiation between the living unit and its environment, an area of being that is associated with concerns of the organic and the inorganic and the origins of life. But, turning to clinical situations, where we can feel more at home, we can refer back to the thirty year old patient in hypnoanalysis who was mentioned in connection with hypnotic settings when he felt himself moving into a watery grave and at the same time had "womb" associations involving the theme of rebirth (Schneck, 28).

There are many symbolic variants of the theme of being in, or trapped in a grave. The feeling of being trapped, with this or with other symbolic equivalents, is common enough, and patients with

lesser or greater degrees of claustrophobic fears seek hypnotic help
often (Schneck, 29). Hypnoanalytic work with one patient in
particular revealed among the determinants of a fear of being in
subways a connection with a real life experience several years be-
before when he was buried in a trench by an Army tank rolling
over him, collapsing the walls of the trench. Afterwards, severe
perceptual distortions set in with experiences, as revealed under
hypnosis, of a quality almost hallucinatory as he identified subway
noises with tank noises, and subway wheels with tank treads. The
overwhelming anxiety in the original military experience, which he
was unable to master at the time, found virtually typical expression
during the hypnotic revivification when he shook and whined,
"Get us out of here! Get us out of here! Dirt's piling in on us!
How'll we get out? Can't get out of here! Stuck! Holla for the guys!
Quick! Tell 'em to get us out!" and so on. In the hypnosis his hands
waved and his head shook.

As with other symptoms, phobic reactions can best be dissipated
when they have not lasted a long time, when secondary gains have
not been well established, when ego strength is comparatively good,
and when the phobic elements are not intimately and significantly
bound up with other disordered aspects of personality functioning.
Often enough patients enter hypnoanalysis with severe phobic
symptomatology that can be modified little if at all. A recent example is that of a man in his thirties, suffering for years from a fear
of traveling alone and remaining alone at home. He would call on
various relatives for assistance and made virtually no efforts to
move beyond the range of a street or two from his home or place of
business. He could be productive in hypnosis as far as reviving past
memories was concerned. He could see significance in a variety of
interrelationships between ideas, feelings, and events. But hypnotic
clarifications and direct encouragement failed to move him significantly to take a chance and make an attempt to tolerate the
anxiety of coming out of his shell even briefly in an effort to stimulate reorganization and promote reconditioning. He served essentially as an example of a not unusual treatment failure. And for him,
as for others, there had been treatment failures before. They number
more by the time hypnoanalysis is sought because so often it is regarded as a last measure with pleadings that it just must succeed.

5. Successes and Failures and Attitudes Toward Treatment

Some patients may seek hypnoanalysis first, before any efforts at non-hypnotic therapy have been made. In certain cases impressions are misleading. The patients consciously or unconsciously may seek it in the belief that it is fundamentally unrealistic and cannot succeed. They may request it with highly unreasonable demands which they sense may prevent its actual use, so that they will have made the gesture of seeking help without really embarking on it. They may believe hypnosis induction will indeed fail for them so that in this way the gesture toward treatment will have been made, but help actually avoided. Such deceptions serve as a reminder here of other deceptive requests for hypnoanalysis to which general reference has already been made. A few examples are given now.

A patient complained of feelings of sexual inadequacy, anxiety, obsessive-compulsive behavior, and a travel phobia. He had been in treatment elsewhere. He denied that gains had been achieved. It was ascertained that he really had doubts about the hypno-analytic approach he was asking for, and felt guilty about changing doctors. His notions about hypnosis were in the realm of wishful thinking. Basically he was not interested in it. Treatment was initiated on a non-hypnotic level, and hypnoanalytic measures were introduced later after they were assessed more realistically.

A middle aged man presented his views about hypnoanalysis, stressing, as one finds often, a highly mechanistic approach. He had made gains in previous non-hypnotic therapy but wanted hypno-analysis for additional betterment. He was rigid and compulsive. He disregarded factual information about hypnotic measures, adhering to his long held fantasies. He agreed, however, to start treatment without hypnosis, a path decided upon because I felt any early work with hypnotic methods would be doomed to failure. Gradually he moved into a hypnoanalysis and made more progress.

A young woman sought hypnoanalysis on the advice of a friend. She felt rejected by her parents and believed they lacked understanding. She complained about anxiety, chest pain, and gastrointestinal upsets. The request for hypnoanalysis on advice of her friend proved to be her way of establishing an initial treatment contact. Specific methods were of no concern to her and she was ready to accept treatment along non-hypnotic lines. It was possible to offer her some early symptomatic relief with hypnosis, however, following which she moved into a hypnoanalysis. After the major work in treatment had been achieved in hypnoanalytic settings, the hypnotic approach was dropped for the final phase. I believe it is important to mention that this sequence is not unusual and I have employed it many times. It is not preplanned. After hypnoanalytic measures have served their purpose in enhancing development of significant changes, patients may appear to do as well thereafter without hypnotic methods. The latter are dropped when they have outlived their usefulness. To persist in employing them compulsively would seem to serve the needs of the therapist rather than those of the patient.

A young woman, depressed and somewhat paranoid, inquired about hypnoanalytic methods but poor ego strength apparent in her at the time, and seemingly present for many years past, prompted the decision to avoid hypnotic techniques. Basically she was seeking aid, the request for hypnosis serving as an impetus to take the step toward treatment. She offered the frequently expressed reason for stressing hypnotic measures. She believed they would decrease total treatment time significantly.

A young man with gastrointestinal discomfort was interested in hypnoanalysis. He had been in treatment before but had discontinued because he had made no progress. Yet it became clear that he ran from it when some of his deeper personality problems were approached. Treatment for him turned out to be an essential failure. Many such patients are very ambivalent toward help of any type. They want it and they do not want it. This ambivalence is common enough. Often, however, the divergent wishes are quite intense and almost impossible to resolve. The fact that, basically, requests for hypnoanalysis may be deceptive to start with does not imply that failure will ensue. Reasons for requesting any form of treatment may be unrealistic and deceptive at first. Yet when treatment is initiated the underlying issues involved in the deceptions may be overcome, good insights established, and progress achieved. On the other hand, despite initial ambivalence and deception, treatment may get under way well, but eventually, for whatever reasons may be involved, failure is the end result.

The depressed and paranoid girl mentioned above received enough support over a period of time so that it was not necessary for her to reenter the hospital to which she had been confined earlier. She was unable, however, to function well enough socially and at work to warrant her continuing to live in a city strange and hostile in her eyes. She had to return to her home elsewhere, and not long afterwards she was hospitalized again. The young man with the gastrointestinal difficulties discontinued his treatment once more when he had to face the fact that his very superficial functioning had to be seen for what it was, were he to improve significantly. Unable to face this, he decided to give up the search for any type of aid. The woman who had sought hypnoanalysis on the advice of her friend, when really seeking some fundamental type of help primarily, hypnosis or no hypnosis as part of it, did improve as has been mentioned. It would be pleasant to say that changes for better or worse can be predicted in advance with reasonable certainty. As is well known, there have been studies on such predictability, but for the clinician, a trial at treatment, with those patients he has been accustomed to work with and on the basis of accumulated experience and developed judgment, is about the best means he can employ in attempting to assess likely success or failure.

The patient who seeks hypnoanalysis claiming it is his last chance, because everything else has failed, is often doomed to fail again. He carries a heavy weight of discouragement into any new situation. As part of this, his demands in regard to fantasied capabilities of hypnoanalytic techniques are grossly exaggerated. An example is a middle aged patient who had been in analysis elsewhere on three different occasions. Hypnoanalysis would be his final effort. He was unable to hold job positions in keeping with his abilities. He feared failure and he feared success. He was self-defeating in decision and action. He was a very obsessive-compulsive individual. While quite complimentary in his expressions toward his previous analyst, it was ascertained that he had left during a phase of negative transference. He adopted a deprecatory attitude toward any seemingly good developments in this new relationship and when, again, he discontinued prematurely, it was with the feeling that he had failed once more.

Extreme discouragement and a negative view toward treatment on the part of the patient must be differentiated from such feelings and views adopted by other clinicians. This is particularly noteworthy with problems that some therapists may find difficult to evaluate. A simple example referable to hypnotherapy, rather than to hypno-analysis specifically, may be given. Whereas hypnotic methods are often helpful in removing amnesia, some clinicians feel uneasy about the validity of the symptom and are reluctant to approach the problem. I encountered several cases with amnesia while in military service and was able to clear most of them (Schneck, 30 31). One patient whom I discussed as representative of a divided personality had presented his problem elsewhere. He was evaluated clinically, the claim of amnesia was brushed aside, and he was labelled a pathological liar. The "diagnosis" was quite incorrect. He was treated, his problems evaluated, and the amnesia was cleared. This occurred in an Army prison where he was confined for desertion. At a later date, another psychiatrist studied his prob-lem with the use of sodium amytal. This evaluation was unknown to me at the time. The findings concurred with mine as I learned from the patient, and then afterwards directly from the psychiatrist involved. Negative views of other clinicians can influence patients in their approach to hypnotherapy and hypnoanalysis. Often they have considerable deleterious impact on patients for whom there is some hope. The attitude of the patient himself is, however, of pri-mary importance. If he can be helped at all, he will be helped if he sees hope regardless of earlier retarding professional opinions.

Patients seeking hypnotherapy with a rigid view of symptom removal or personality change in a special direction may accept no deviation from a fantasy of direct course of action to achieve these ends. If they are fortunate and their personalities such that the capabilities are there, and in the absence of contraindications of personality features precluding attainment of these ends, the results may be quite happy. It would be nice to say that such fortunate patients are frequently encountered. The fact is that they are not. The demands are made but the rewards are not easy to come by. On the other hand, patients have the opportunity to enter hypno-analysis with the understanding, stated or implied, that this treat-ment approach can serve to help elucidate motivations and goals in relation to problems viewed from broader perspectives. Entering treatment on this basis is consistent with parallel therapeutic experience in the broader field of psychotherapy. Hypnoanalytic measures furnish opportunities for clarification of motivation and goal (Schneck, 32).

6. Motivation and Goal, Intellectual and Emotional Insight

A forty-year-old woman was interested in singing, and she served as a vocalist in various entertainment settings. The financial rewards were appealing but her anxieties were increasing. When she was young her father told her she might become a tramp if she became an entertainer. Her confusion, and that of her parents, was highlighted in certain hypnotic verbalizations. She told of a request by her school principal to sing with a group of young people. She did well and they won a prize. Then, "I'm afraid—what if I can't sing like I should. Will I compromise. I made a compromise with my father. I made a compromise when I married. Then my father said how wonderful it is to have a voice. Men will fall in love with you. Oh! He was such a mixed-up man. He made me so mixed-up. I feel I never sang well in front of people. Such fear in me! Such guilt! It was so amazing to me to make money by singing. Such guilt! Yet I had a drive to do it. Like I was fighting my father! I had to fight my mother too! Yet, now she is anxious for me to sing . . ."

Other verbalizations of this patient may be offered as examples of the manner in which some patients speak and think and assess themselves in the hypnotic settings. The very sounds of the evaluations do not register as remarkably different from those in non-hypnotic sessions, although they do differ in quality and in the depth of emotional involvement in the same patient from the verbalizations in non-hypnotic exchanges.

"I never was nervous at my husband's club. I felt it was the only way I could impress people." She had trouble with high notes and was asked whether they had special meaning for her. "I feel if I let go I can sing high notes. I'm afraid to let go because I feel I'll lose control of myself . . . The minute I get into the high notes I grow tense. Then all of a sudden they come out. They're wonderful. I can do it when I'm alone." During the following session, the same topic was approached in hypnosis. "There's something churning but I don't know what it is. All week a thought kept coming to me that I identify singing and sex and the taboos about it—like I identify high notes with letting go and sex, and that I should let go and not try to control it. I'm not free in sex or in anything else. I don't know how to break free. When I forget myself and let go they come right out. I try to control it like I was controlled for years by my father."

She spoke of her distaste for sexual relations with her husband. "There's a feeling of dirtiness linked up with it. I have that feeling about singing. In a group I'm afraid to sing out for fear of calling attention to myself. I sing low." Regarding the issue of making a sexual display of herself, "I never thought I was making a sexual display of myself but I realize now that that's what I feel I do. Oh yes! That's why there's so much guilt attached to it." She told of a particular event involving a specific band leader. "Sure I was making a sexual display of myself through singing." A woman admired her and said she had "it." "That's what I'm afraid of in front of people. If I open up my throat for the high notes it would be like a sexual display." Later on she revealed, "I used to have deadly fears of being a fallen woman. The idea fascinates me now. Sex must be a terrible thing in my life. It's only when (my husband) becomes violently angry that I submit. Even (my singing teacher) frightened me. When I started to sing freely he'd say, 'Now you're thrilling me. Now you excite me . . .' I was frightened when he said that. I think that's why I changed to a woman teacher."

Many points that the patient brought up in hypnosis from time to time had been consciously available to her before. She was impressed by the greater emotional significance they seemed to have for her in the hypnoanalytic interviews. This reaction is encountered often, though not consistently. It is not unusual for patients to obtain emotional insight first during such sessions, with intellectual insight to follow, if one wishes to differentiate between the two in this way. Generally, in relation to non-hypnotic therapy, one encounters reference to the reverse order of experience.

The patient mentioned above, from whose sessions some excerpts were given, demonstrated the utilization of a hypnoanalytic approach that did not entail the use of complex hypnotic devices. The important point is that such an approach can be incorporated into treatment with relative ease by a properly trained psycho-therapist. This simply reflects one of a variety of methods that can lend depth and range to treatment far beyond delimited, stereo-typed concepts of hypnotherapy and hypnoanalysis. The present patient used hypnosis well for absorbing and integrating data that had previously been available to her but had not become funda-mentally a part of her.

7. Variations in Spontaneous Verbalizations

This patient was able to speak freely often, and without special and frequent guidance. Many others function this way too. Some patients require more active participation by the hypnoanalyst and situations must be structured for them. Scenes may have to be described, for example, in order to have the patient proceed to play a role within them, one from which they may then learn as they attempt to view occurrences first somewhat objectively, and then with a sense of emotionl participation and subjective involvement. Patients who stutter are frequently reluctant to verbalize without much guidance during hypnosis sessions. Despite claims of timidity about speaking freely, they may take command and fend off inter-ruptions when hypnosis is not used. In hypnosis they want to be told what to do.

A patient in his late thirties grew anxious about his speech as he anticipated each interview (Schneck, 33). In hypnosis he was told that he would see a scene that would represent in some way, directly or indirectly, the nature of his problem as it pertained to anxiety and speech difficulty when anticipating his office visits. He saw himself walking down a flight of steps, into a dark basement, and he became increasingly frightened with the feeling that some-one was down there. Finally he saw the person but could not identify him. When pressed, the image of his father became clear. The hypnoanalyst-father identification was developed, and this was linked to his fear of authority figures. He specifically identified the walk down the stairs with delving for sexual material, and he saw the hypnotic experience as a reactivation of childhood anxieties and guilt about masturbation and its discovery by his father. The patient claimed that following this discovery in childhood there was an extreme intensification of his speech problem.

8. Dreams and Hypnoanalysis

During hypnoanalysis, when patients say they do not dream at night, or dream little now, and when posthypnotic suggestions are given to stimulate such dreaming, the first product brought to treatment thereafter often has considerable emotional impact. An example is that of a twenty-eight year old man who was furnishing no dreams in treatment and who did not supply one after the initial posthypnotic suggestion. When this suggestion was reenforced, he had a nightmare. He was in a building with other men and they were manacled. Then they were removed from the building and lined up against a wall to be killed. The patient managed to escape. The three other men were killed by shooting with a machine gun and the killings were done apparently by two women. The patient reached a barn nearby. It was open at both sides. He feared being poisoned there by the two women who had killed the men. During the interpretation of the dream he saw the symbolism as reflecting the view that his wife and mother had been responsible for killing off his father, brother, and father-in-law. His brother was, in fact, still living. The basic issue involved in this interpersonal struggle centered on the degree of his dependency on his wife and mother. He resented their attempts to control him.

When hypnosis is not used and a dream is told, some details appear to be recalled during the telling after having been forgotten on waking. Even if it is regarded as doubtful that these embellishments had been present in the original dreaming, they are nevertheless dealt with because of their inferred dynamic significance. In hypnoanalytic work, a nocturnal dream may be related prior to a hypnosis session. Then, often enough, with the induction of hypnosis, forgotten details of the dream are added, and are dealt with in the way just mentioned. This filling in of detail is a common occurrence. The impact of an initial nocturnal dream, after posthypnotic suggestion for dreaming and after claims of alleged absence of dreaming, bears resemblances to the importance of the first dream presented in any form of treatment whether it involves hypnosis or not. There are parallels here to the recollections of first memories from childhood in terms of dynamic significance. An initial hypnotically induced dream or spontaneous hypnotic dream in the early phase of a hypnoanalysis warrants careful examination too. A cluster of important personality ingredients is frequently represented in these productions.

The patient whose dream was just described revealed shortly thereafter some sensations in the realm of sensory and motor phenomena discussed earlier in this book. He felt his entire body getting very large, his hands and arms getting heavier, and the weight of his limbs pressing down on the chair. He felt like the large statue of the Lincoln Memorial. These sensations, he said, had occurred previously in hypnosis, and with their spontaneous appearance then he thought of the connection between Lincoln and the theme of humility. He connected both with his father, now dead. In hypnosis he would become tearful when mentioning his father. The spontaneous sensory experience was part of a reactivation and expression of emotional associations and ties to his father that he generally kept in check rather firmly through repression or suppression.

9. Doctor-patient Relationships and Behavior

In assessing clinical change, especially improvement, things are not always what they seem, and the analyst's wishful thinking can play a role in coloring a patient's status too brightly. I have found often that hypnosis can cut through outward appearances in ways that are sharp and decisive, revealing a patient's status to be quite different from what seems evident on the surface. A patient, for example, experienced consciously an easing of his feelings of depression. The product of an hypnotic experience pointed, however, to a guarded prognosis. It arose during a hypnoanalytic session following that in which he expressed his feeling of improvement. When he entered hypnosis he was told that he would see something he wanted very much. He waw a body on a table. It was covered with a white cloth. He saw grey hair and he saw the person's shoes. The position of the body's legs seemed similar to his own as he lay on the couch. The body with its white covering reminded him of a hospital or morgue, and it was apparently dead. As he inspected it, he had trouble identifying this body, but when asked whether he really felt he knew who it was he identified it as his own. The scene disturbed him very much and he talked then about sickness, old age, and death.

As fragments from such cases are given now, it is worth reporting that some patients function better in treatment with certain techniques that differ from those more effective for other patients. Hypnotic methods must be evaluated not only in terms of broad, general applicability, but also from the view of special suitability for a particular patient. When used flexibly in this way, a variety of dynamisms can be elucidated in subtle fashion in contrast to the more obvious, clear cut impact often recounted of the effect of hypnosis in releasing repressed material, generally in the form of buried memories. It is commonplace, in fact, to see the elucidation through hypnotic techniques, of mechanisms of isolation, identification, projection and introjection, symbolization, displacement, condensation, rationalization, and others.

In hypnoanalysis, as with any form of treatment, one must consider the nature of the patient's behavior and his productions in relation to the structure of the treatment situation, his expectations, the interests and expectations of the therapist, the ingredients of the doctor-patient relationship, and similar concerns. The type of hypnoanalytic relationship that unfolds is related to the personalities and methods of operation of both the patient and the hypnoanalyst. Nevertheless, the personality of the patient and his special type of hypnotic functioning plays a powerful role in what emerges even aside from the basic attributes of the hypnoanalyst. Similar techniques employed by the hypnoanalyst on different occasions, with apparently similar attitudes on his part, evoke differing responses from different patients, no less the same patient from time to time. This, of course, is not remarkably different from other types of treatment situations, but I think the total picture of a series of hypnoanalytic encounters with a variety of patients will vary more in their appearance than will a series of therapeutic situations entailing more rigid, standardized, conventional psychoanalytic attitudes. One may add that the latter also vary more than is generally acknowledged. When some patients seek hypnoanalysis after a supposedly classical psychoanalytic treatment, it seems evident that it is classical or traditional only in so far as the previous analyst might have enjoyed calling it so. What takes place in fact is often far different, I believe many would agree, than what is alleged to have taken place in the determination to satisfy orthodox strictures or the demands of group affiliations.

The manner in which a patient behaves in treatment does have some relationship to what the patient believes his doctor expects of him, and one of the areas stressed by others in this connection is the nature of the dreams he presents. Not long ago a study was made of the dream that the patient tells (34). It is no surprise that at least in some cases dreams involving features that the patient thinks might elicit a negative response tend not to be recalled. The process of dream reporting is influenced by the stated concern of the doctor in the dreams of the moment, and by the relationship between the patient and the doctor at the time of the interview. It is not unusual, however, for dreams withheld to be revealed soon thereafter in hypnosis by virtue of the effect of the hypnotic process on repressive mechanisms within the framework of the hypnotic transference. The hypnotic aspects of the transference itself, including procedural features and associated fantasies, often find their way into the fabric of many dreams. The notion, however, that hypnosis can be understood only in terms of the hypnotic subject behaving in a manner that he believes is expected of him is, in the light of my hypnoanalytic experience and of others too I should say, a rather shallow and incorrect assessment of the hypnotic setting when implied or taken as a valid generalization.

10. Spontaneous Remissions

Another theme involving critical scrutiny of what happens in treatment or as a result of treatment is that of spontaneous remission (35). The question posed at times is whether psychotherapy does indeed assist patients significantly. In fact, does it really help at all, or are improvements basically a matter of spontaneous remission, only seemingly influenced by whatever psychotherapy had been engaged in. Is improvement really a function of time (36)? The question must be asked in the case of hypnoanalysis, as for psychoanalysis with its various orientations and for psychotherapy with divergent approaches.

When treatment is time consuming I believe the question is most valid. The hypnoanalyst must ask himself in all honesty whether the patient might not have improved with time as a result of spontaneous psychological reorganization even if the latter might have differed in some ways from the changes ascribed to the hypno-analysis. Such spontaneous change can and does take place. Yet hypnoanalytic work can influence the patient in many ways in terms of a meaningful interpersonal relationship assisting him, even though in the equivalent time period the patient might have im-proved on his own in some way in terms of subjective feelings of greater comfort.

It is true that the patient normally encounters people and events potentially capable of helping him in some fashion toward feelings of betterment. When treatment lasts a relatively short while, how-ever, and when the patient has felt miserable for years without sig-nificant spontaneous improvement, the issue of such change now, primarily based on the passage of time, becomes questionable al-though possible. In addition, there are situations especially refer-able to hypnoanalysis, or to hypnotherapy involving certain tech-niques aimed at resolving special problems. Here, a phobia per-sisting for months or longer may be resolved in a matter of hours or days. An amnesia persisting for days, months, or years, may be cleared within a matter of minutes or hours. Anxiety, unabated for months or years, may be significantly dispelled in a few sessions or less. In such situations, statistical inplications casting doubt on the effec-tiveness of the therapeutic measures make the greatest impression only on the statistician involved and on his co-workers. They are without significance otherwise. To repeat, however, if a more diffuse complaint such as anxiety or depression has been present for weeks, months or years, and hypnoanalysis or some other treatment tech-niques in turn continue for years, let us say, the issue of spontaneous remission cannot be ignored. Even here, nevertheless, one cannot dismiss in the face of spontaneous alteration of symptoms of anxiety or depression, the rewards of treatment contact for the patient in ways not necessarily allied pointedly to the diffuse complaints of anxiety and depression. These seemingly secondary rewards in rela-tion to personality change and modes of functioning cannot be dis-regarded as meaningless by-products.

11. Hypnoanalysis and Psychoanalytic Explorations

If one can speak of secondary rewards in this way for the pa-tient, one can feel justified in thinking in such terms for the psychotherapist as a clinical investigator during his hypnoanalytic work. The rewards consist of the growing body of information regarding personality functioning in general, and specific understandings of individual symptoms. I have already made reference to this earlier in the book. Some additional examples may be offered. A patient in hypnoanalysis recalled during a hypnosis session his experiences of micropsia as a child. An evaluation of these experiences, integrating them with much else learned about the patient during the course of treatment, permitted further clarification of this curious and interesting symptom the psychodynamics of which had been investigated relatively little before. The most meaningful integration of these understandings was with data presented earlier as an outgrowth of psychoanalytic formulations.

The patient, in his fifties, described during hypnosis how, between the ages of six and eight, he observed all objects in his room getting smaller and smaller with an impression of movement resulting in these objects eventually appearing very small and far off in the distance. In relation to them, he would be comparatively large. "It was like looking through the wrong end of a telescope." Then, suddenly the objects would return to their normal size. He felt frightened and intensely alone. During the course of the hypnoanalysis it became clear that his micropsia seemed to reflect the patient's expansive needs, counteracting a closed-in feeling. It was a reaction to heavy psychological pressures. It reflected an attempt to cope with intense, repressed anger. He was symbolically manipulating people identified as objects. He was exercising control in an effort to cope with feelings of weakness and insecurity. The micropsia was a mirror of his feeling of separation from people and things about him during his childhood years. It was an outgrowth of diminishing ego strength at that time, with defenses reenforced later. Oral and aggressive components evident in this patient were found to be present also in cases studied by psychoanalysts who issued reports elsewhere (Schneck, 37).

On another occasion it was possible to study certain aspects of déjà vu in a patient as a result of material he introduced during hypnoanalytic sessions, and to evaluate this material in relation to observations made by others (38-40). Freud saw déjà vu implying an earlier unconscious impression making its way into consciousness as a result of a current, similar impression. He mentioned déjà vu as a counterpart of depersonalization and derealization since an attempt is made to accept something as belonging to the ego instead of furthering its exclusion. I suggested it might be more correct to say that déjà vu reflects only in part an attempt at acceptance. More accurately, there seemed to be involved some ambivalence associated with recognizing an area of conflict that lies at the core of the phenomenon. The theme of ambivalence seemed more pertinent than the claim by Fenichel that repression was completed in déjà vu, the ego not wanting to be reminded of the repressed material, and déjà vu appearing as a result of being reminded contrary to its will (Schneck, 41).

The patient, when thirty-eight years old, recalled during a hypnoanalytic session that he had the first déjà vu experience when he was eleven. He was very angry with his mother, had a temper tantrum, and destroyed some prized possessions. He thought of this as a symbolic substitute for suicide. It was at the point of this destruction that the first déjà vu set in. The usual pattern thereafter was for the episodes to occur in a social setting when he was in "intimate" conversation with others. Accompanying the déjà vu aura was a feeling of its association with previous dreams. The aura involved the feeling that "something awful was going to happen." When his dreams were investigated it was learned during hypnoanalytic sessions that certain dreams of a specific nature seemed to be most relevant to the déjà vu. They concerned homosexual or heterosexual situations when he would wish for erections of "immense proportions." His penis would increase in size, then break, becoming completely detached from his body, leaving him mutilated. This was the "something awful" that was going to happen. He would develop nightmarish anxiety. The déjà vu for this patient appeared to be linked closely with castration anxiety which was reflected also in other aspects of his personality functioning. It seemed to be in part a dream substitute, accounting for the feeling of some connection with previous nocturnal dreams.

In another patient a point arose with an interesting association to the theme and déjà vu. The relationship between déjà vu and previous nocturnal dreams has been touched on by others. In this one patient I encountered the phenomenon of a feeling of déjà vu experienced within a nocturnal dream itself. Exploration revealed certain connections between the aura and previous happenings in his real life settings. He was being treated at the time with short-term psychotherapy in which hypnotherapy was included in a successful effort to eliminate excessive smoking. Certain aspects of the symptom and its removal were linked to the déjà vu feeling (Schneck, 42).

12. Automatic, Compulsive, and Impulsive Drawing

Allied to the theme of hypnoanalytic work furnishing an opportunity for gaining additional insights into psychodynamics of personality functioning not necessarily related specifically to hypnotic settings as such, is the additional theme of evaluating the direct influence of hypnotic settings in exploring further certain activities used as part of personality study generally unassociated with hypnosis. An example is automatic drawing (Schneck, 43). Drawing procedures have long been employed as part of psychodiagnostic evaluations made during the course of personality study for the purpose of assessing treatment needs. Usually such drawings are part of larger psychological test procedures. The hypnotic setting can affect the nature of such drawings and I have touched on this before. Hypnotic automatic drawing may be used additionally, however, as part of an over-all treatment procedure. It can be incorporated into a hypnoanalysis. One may employ it to assist patients in clarifying their behavior. The automaticity of manual movements is similar to that found in automatic writing. Such drawing is to be distinguished from compulsive drawing. Occasionally it will be found that when a patient is given pencil and paper under hypnosis, he may proceed to draw rather rapidly, seemingly without thinking carefully about what he is putting down on paper. He may repeat the process after halting intermittently. There appears to be a compulsive and also an impulsive quality to his behavior. Automatic drawing that bears a similarity to automatic writing is generally done more slowly. Similarly, the initial productions may be vague and ill-formed and difficult to interpret. More cohesive and definable productions emerge in time. It is not unusual, however, for some patients to produce the latter almost immediately.

Subjects show varying degrees of aptitude when drawing automatically under hypnosis. Also, this variation appears in connection with automatic drawing done posthypnotically following appropriate hypnotic suggestions. Such drawing can be produced in self-hypnotic states too. The complexity of drawings varies from subject to subject and in the same subject from time to time.

In hypnoanalysis one is generally more interested in the story that the drawings tell the patient in connection with his personality functioning. Less attention is paid to psychodiagnostic issues more pertinent to diagnostic testing settings. The latter involve more attention to characteristics of the drawings such as size, position on paper, white space utilization, erasures, broken lines, and related ingredients. Aside from the interest inherent in comparisons of regular drawings by patients and their hypnotic drawings without instructions for automaticity, and such drawings involving instructions for automaticity, there is the additional interest that may be explored regarding the comparisons between automatic drawing and doodling. This, however, takes us somewhat afield from our immediate hypnoanalytic concerns.

Often, automatic drawings seen in isolation are difficult to interpret within the framework of the patient's operations at that particular time. When they are continued through several sessions, however, clarification occurs when the series of drawings is examined. They may be compared to other types of activity focussing on symbolic processes and the dynamic unconscious. The series is like a series of dreams which possesses a dynamic interrelatedness that can best be understood when viewing the entire sequence. This would apply also to a series of fantasies. In essence, as far as analytic procedure is concerned, a basic comparison might be to a series of free associations the underlying themes of which become evident only after a lapse of time, when enough has been said to establish a trend or pattern now seen as a whole after smaller pieces or ingredients had been offered in an apparently disconnected fashion.

One may ask about the point of bothering about a series of automatic drawings or some similar procedure if it seems warranted to claim a comparison between such productions and a series of dreams, especially since the dreams can generally be obtained with less trouble. The answer here applies to the point that has been made before. There are many ways to attempt to understand people and to try to help them. It is not a matter of one procedure being necessarily better than another. If, however, certain approaches are not fruitful for some patients at a particular time others may be substituted. Patients vary in what they can do or learn to do. One cannot expect them all to fit one mold. A simple procedure for one may be difficult for another. A patient may produce hypnotic dreams more easily than he can supply nocturnal dreams. He may furnish automatic writings or drawings more easily than information in a simple conversational exchange. He may, in general, work better in hypnosis than without it, and if the reverse is indeed true there would be no point in employing a hypnotic setting for him.

13. Reactions to Hypnotic Behavior and Settings as Reflections of Personality Attributes

Stillerman (44) has put into words what has been implied here repeatedly and what every experienced hypnotherapist knows. In non-hypnotic therapy and in hypnotherapy the patient deals with the therapeutic setting in a way that reflects his basic personality problems. In hypnotherapy, however, his reactions often emerge clearly in the first few trance settings. Frequently, important personality ingredients show up clearly in the very first hypnosis session. Hypnosis is like a catalytic agent and the first or second induction reactions have been compared to the first dream presented by a patient in analytic therapy. Stillerman points out that repressed anxieties, attitudes and impulses come to the surface directly or in disguised forms in hypnosis. Patients may not be consciously aware of the significance of these reactions but the defensive structure surrounding his conflicts may be potentially penetrated and he does react one way or another. These reactions from the start establish at least a tentative relationship, positive or negative, with his therapist.

I can furnish an example, at this point, of a patient seen recently. He had a strong reaction to a first hypnoanalytic session. He verbalized his feelings at the meeting following the initial hypnotic experience. He said he did not know whether he had really entered hypnosis. He discussed this point and then mentioned spontaneously some happenings which gave him the feeling that he really may have been hypnotized. He referred desparagingly to previous non-hypnotic treatment elsewhere and wondered whether the present contact would be essentially the same. He offered some caustic and patently unreasonable comments about differences in fees now and before. Parenthetically it should be noted that he was treated then through a clinic in contrast to the current private practice setting for which the charge was quite average. He was reminded of a few more criticisms that some patients offer in their feelings of disappointment following initial hypnosis sessions and he willingly and almost humorously picked up these protests to add to his own. The issues involved were discussed at length. This is what the patient learned, in summary, and as a result of the discussion, with the realization that his reactions, positive or negative, to a structured hypnotic induction can serve a constructive purpose and assist in an over-all personality evaluation.

First, he found it convenient to find fault with the hypnotic setting. This offered him good reason to think of quitting treatment completely. He would leave with the assertion, to convince himself and others, that he really tried a different form of treatment and that it was not good. In this way he would retain problems about which he had mixed feelings. They furnished him with an outlet for sexual exhibitionistic trends, and he was not wholly convinced that he should change in this respect. He was reluctant to think of himself as really "abnormal." Second, the feelings of aggression he experienced when making his accusations were quite pronounced, especially the show of aggression toward me. This was in sharp contrast to his behavior during the few previous interviews. Most important in this regard was his claim and belief that he was simply unable to feel strongly about anything at any time. He loved no one and nothing and he could not be truly angry, he said, about anything. Now the patient of his own accord mentioned the fact that this situation pointed up a show of emotion that contradicted the earlier view he had expressed of himself. Third, it was pointed out to him that at times some patients are concerned about their submissiveness. They identify this trait with compliance in hypnotic settings and with the associated feeling of being controlled. They link submissiveness with homosexuality. It is evident that such statements cannot be offered to all patients, but it seemed on the basis of previous interviews with him, that the remarks might possibly have significance. They did. He nodded his head in agreement even before the comments were concluded. Thus, it is important to realize that hypnotic behavior and reactions to such behavior are fundamentally a part of a total interpersonal contact in hypnoanalytic work and must be integrated into the processes of treatment that includes both hypnotic and non-hypnotic sessions. For other patients, depending upon circumstances at the time, all of the points mentioned above might be dealt with within additional hypnosis settings that can be established almost invariably despite the aggression and criticism by the patients, and despite sincere allegations of their failure as hypnotic subjects.

14. Anxiety, Hypnoanalysis, and Somatic Symptomatology

Hypnoanalysis, in addition to dealing with emotions, in terms of their psychological expression, can be employed to evaluate and treat somatic manifestations of emotional conflict (Schneck, 45). A patient in his thirties complained of extrasystoles, premature beats dating back twenty years to his adolescence. He felt the strong cardiac impulses as "skipping" and feared the possibility of eventual cardiac damage and sudden death. He reacted with anxiety. The chest sensations would occur on an average of twenty times a day. He was always reassured, but unsuccessfullly so, by his physicians who confirmed his physical fitness while explaining the abnormal cardiac beats detected on electrocardiographic tracings. The patient entered treatment to explore emotional involvements.

It was possible to elucidate direct connections between occurrences of the premature beats with states of tension and anxiety. As his tension eased, episodes of abnormal beats varied in frequency of occurrence and then diminished. Concern about his health was evaluated in terms of certain identifications with his deceased father, and with his mother's death as a result of a heart attack. He used the symptom to further his passive needs which in turn were part of conflict over submissiveness and a desire for independence. Failures could be rationalized on the basis of physical malfunctioning and he evoked sympathy in this way. His tension, with the accompanying extrasystoles, was linked to a masoschistic relationship with a mother-in-law, ill as his mother had been, with hypertension. During his hypnoanalysis it was found that when he was in hypnosis this patient experienced enhanced recall, less obsessiveness, greater spontaneity, more emotional involvement with material elicited when compared with non-hypnotic functioning, and improved ability to integrate emerging data.

Regarding the issue of employing any psychotherapeutic measure for concerns related to cardiac function as described here, there is ample evidence and justification for it in the light of earlier evaluations of emotions in connection with cardiac activity (46). Some studies have been done also on the effect of hypnotic suggestion on the heart beat (47). In the same way that evaluations have been made of the emotional involvements with cardiovascular functioning, so too have they been assessed in connection with the operations of other organ systems. One of the central themes has been the role of anxiety in somatic dysfunction. I am inclined to think that in the patient with extrasystoles mentioned above, reduction in the level of anxiety was of predominant weight in diminishing the number of premature beats. The details of psychodynamic issues that were clarified were of aid to the patient in terms of his over-all personality functioning, but only indirectly in so far as any influence on the cardiac beat was concerned. The anxiety reduction and symptom relief were allied to the concept of psychogenic organ dysfunction in the realm of somatization reactions through operations of the autonomic nervous apparatus. The psychodynamic issues touched on hysterical components of the problem, with special reference to mechanisms of repression and identification. It is not necessary to go into detail about these points here except to observe that the division just noted between hysterical conversions and psychogenic somatizations can be arbitrary and artificial at times.

15. Dependency, Action, and Magic in Hypnotherapy and Psychoanalysis

Bowers, Berkowitz, and Brecher, when discussing hypnosis in another context and with special reference to severely dependent states, commented that acute panic and a deteriorating trend in their patients seemed to be stemmed as a result of their developing the feeling that something was actively being done for them (48). I believe this is often true for many types of patients, though of course not invariably so, regardless of the problems and of the particular therapeutic measures employed. The feeling depends much on the nature of the transference. The patient with extra-systoles had been in treatment before with others and felt he had not been helped. He expressed a lack of faith in psychiatric treatment. This attitude is expressed often by patients seeking hypnotherapy or hypnoanalysis. I believe the use of hypnosis has an implication for them of something specific being done to them. It is not just a matter of talking. There may be talking, as they see it, but it is talking and doing. It has magical connotations to a degree, but this is not important as long as the therapist is aware of it along with his considerable awareness of other dynamic issues. The hypnoanalyst can, in appropriate cases, capitalize on the magical connotations and eventually, in helping the patient, eliminate the need for reliance on the magical themes and effect realistic reorientations. One must remember that the magical element in treatment is present in the views of many patients regarding so many forms of therapy, not necessarily hypnotherapy, and not necessarily psychotherapy. Psychotherapy and psychoanalysis possess powerful magical configurations for patients. In hypnotherapy, the hypnotic procedure is one area with magical connotations. In psychoanalysis, the areas of interpretation with special reference to sex and dreams and the use of the couch are invested with magical connotations.

16. Concentrated Hypnoanalytic Measures and Transference Implications

One is generally more optimistic about efforts to assist patients with problems of relatively short duration as compared to those of long duration. It does not follow that results are invariably better in the former category, but in general the likelihood of achieving more rapid change is greater in such cases, especially when ego strength is good. A pertinent example is that of a woman in her thirties with increasing fatigue over a period of one and a half to two years and with accentuation of the problem during the preceding eight months. There was considerable dyspnea when walking one city block, climbing a flight of stairs, running only half a block. Hypnoanalytic investigations showed the symptoms to be based on intense, long standing psychological conflict. Currently, the difficulties were related to pressing problems now on hand and linked with concerns dating back to her earlier years. The latter involved long repressed feelings related to her having been told that her birth had not been planned. This tied in with her indecision about becoming pregnant. Both points were connected with mixed feelings toward her parents. Her conscious and unconscious views of them were markedly different and especially troublesome to her. The symbolic connotation of her symptoms was of deterioration and dying. They denoted a trend toward self-destruction. The symptoms of one and a half to two years duration were dissipated within a few hours of treatment and improvement has been maintained for fifteen years. Visual imagery entailing dream-like qualities proved to be of help in the hypnoanalytic technical maneuvers. Induced auditory hallucinations were also employed.

I believe it may be of interest to summarize the content of her hypnoanalytic experience in this one area without becoming involved in an evaluation of the psychodynamics. The latter are of general interest, needless to say, but the hypnotic happenings are more pertinent now for illustrative purposes.

The patient entered hypnosis easily. She was told to think of a song of her own choice, to concentrate on it, then gradually to hear it. She would move along with it then in thought and mood. She hallucinated "Smoke Gets In Your Eyes," hearing it played first by an orchestra, then by a man at a piano. Following this she saw herself at a recently visited summer resort. She saw the mountains and lake. She was in a canoe by herself. Everything was bleak and somber. The canoe overturned and she fell into the water's depths without struggling. "Then I drowned." That evening, guests went about their activities as if nothing had happened. "Nobody missed me." "Strangely enough, however, *I* was sitting on the porch . . . looking at the lake."

The patient was told she would hear music again. She believed then that a radio had actually been turned on loudly, nearby. This was not so. She hallucinated "St. Louis Blues." She was watching a pianist perform. Then she saw herself walking in a field of grass. She came to a precipice. She turned around and saw to her "horror" a man wearing a cap. He pushed her and she fell into a body of water but managed to keep her head above the surface, wondering how to escape in view of the rapids nearby and the man perched above, on his stomach, hands outstretched, to push her again should she climb up toward him.

She was asked who the man was "I don't know; I've never seen him before!" Dr.: "Keep looking and you'll recognize him." With considerable emotion that seemed to be an admixture of fear, perplexity, consternation and anguish, she shouted, "It's my father! And he's leering down at me!" She was encouraged to climb the mountain despite her claims that it was too difficult and that her limbs were getting scratched. "I can't make it!" But she was urged on. She feared the encounter with her father, so she was encouraged to talk to him, to ask him the reason for all of this. She kept sobbing and pleading with him. To her horror and amazement he kept repeating, "I hate you and I want to kill you"

The patient managed somehow to get to the top of the cliff. She ran away and her father followed. Tearfully and with anxiety she questioned him again. He expressed his feeling of hate once more but added now that she had been an inconvenience to him and that he had really wished to leave her mother for other women. He wanted to be "free." Suddenly the patient was horror stricken when watching her father become transformed into her mother who looked at her menacingly, asserting that the patient had been an inconvenience to her. Finally she saw her mother and father as one person, leering at her.

After this, the patient dreamed all over again a repetitive, nocturnal dream that she had previously reported. She was a little girl at home, hiding under the bed. Her mother ran back and forth, looking for her to "kill" her. She "hugged the floor in fright." She saw her mother's shoes as she saw them in the visualization a little earlier when her father became transformed into her mother. In real life, as a child she had been chased by her mother in a similar scene with her hiding under the bed. Then, of course, she had feared being beaten.

In hypnosis still, the patient regressed spontaneously to the age of twelve. There was her mother in the kitchen, baking bread. Her father returned from work, wearing the same cap as in the cliff scene. It was a happy setting. She told them of a bad dream regarding her father wanting to kill her. There she sat telling it, holding her doll. She told of the cliff episode. Her mother was amused and laughed. Her father felt hurt. "How could you dream such a thing when I love you, have always been good to you, and have never set a hand on you to hurt you?"

The patient was instructed to look into a mirror. She saw herself approaching it but then shouted, "No! I don't want to look." In the mirror she saw "a monster, grizzly, bleary-eyed, a large amount of hair, frightful." It looked like "Mr. Hyde." In hypnosis her hand suddenly lashed out. "With my fist I smashed the mirror!" She buried her head in her lap and cried. She was encouraged to look into another mirror but refused and had to be encouraged again. When she saw the same monster, she was instructed to converse with him and to ask who he was. "I'm the real you—the mean and hateful you." She protested but he affirmed his stand. He confirmed her parents' attitude of regarding her as an inconvenience. "What do you want me to do?" "Die! Die! Die!" She cried in anguish and after a while a change came over her spontaneously. Amidst tears she shouted, "I have a right to be here! It wasn't my fault I was born!" She repeated this over and over, sobbing and then laughing in defiance. "I'm not afraid of you! It's not my fault! I have every right to be here!" The image of the monster grew smaller and smaller. Eventually it was very tiny. Then it disappeared.

Spontaneously, the patient described herself at her adult age level and experienced a great sense of relief. Her tears disappeared and her anxiety was replaced by a sense of calm. She visualized herself with her husband, happy and content. The hypnotic events had a profound effect on her and this was quite evident in all of her activities immediately thereafter. One encounters patients who tend to be dramatically involved in hypnoanalytic sessions in this way (Schneck, 49). As I have mentioned before, they are in a minority. The session content can be fascinating, but in terms of good, long lasting effects, the dramatic components do not in themselves serve as indicators necessarily of results to be achieved.

I am inclined to believe that the nature of the hypnoanalytic events, in the case of the woman with dyspnea and associated psychological difficulties, would come to view most likely when certain transference elements had already become part of the doctor-patient relationship. This relationship might exist for a short or a long time, but I believe the ingredients must be there. For example, I doubt that such hypnotic productions would emerge during the first contact of a patient with his hypnoanalyst. The patient would not be sufficiently secure to permit the emergence of such affect charged material involving ties with both parents. In a more superficial way, dramatic happenings with comparable affect, but without the complex ingredients, can emerge and have emerged in combat neuroses of wartime settings. In the present example, certain aspects of identification of the hypnoanalyst with both parents, mother and father, plus additional realistic ingredients associated with the therapist, probably permitted the patient to deal with her problem this way. Here then, the nature of the transference is important. Speaking of the transference however, is a matter different, in my opinion, from speaking about trance. Thus, Watkins comments that when the hypnotherapist speaks of trance and the psychoanalyst speaks of transference, they are talking about the same thing (50). He adds that the hypnotherapist often does not know that he is dealing with transference and the psychoanalyst often is unaware that he is in contact with his patient in terms of the latter's "light trance ego state." This theme of the core of hypnosis has been taken up in earlier pages when discussing theoretical issues mainly, and I shall not repeat the remarks here. I might point out parenthetically that there has been increasing interest in this issue. A pertinent example is the report by Kurauchi and Fujita (56). Suffice it to say that I see transference concerns as an ingredient of some aspects of hypnosis in special settings, but transference does not constitute the fundamental nature of hypnosis as such.

17. Interviews with the Therapist in Fantasy, Transference and Countertransference

In recent years I have done some work involving an extension of scene visualization and related techniques. This extension consists of the hypnotic patient conversing with the therapist in fantasy (Schneck, 51). Patients can manipulate the session in a way which establishes a duality in their functioning through which they attempt to probe and contend with unconscious, contradictory tensions. By viewing the therapist in the hypnotic fantasy they distort him in various ways while depicting the distortions in terms of his appearance and conversation within the visual and auditory manifestations of the hypnotic fantasy. Mechanisms of projection and identification, especially, come into view and their utilization by the patient becomes more evident. The hypnoanalyst is helped into a position of observing this more clearly. Not only does he note the operations of the patient, but he is in a position through clarification of his image by the patient to observe himself more clearly through the patient's eyes and in this way to take note of countertransference factors of which he himself may not have been fully aware up until then. A patient may not reveal to him by a direct remark what he imparts indirectly through a conversation with the figure of the therapist in fantasy. The technique may be of help at points where the hypnoanalyst feels he is functioning too blindly and where he believes the patient may show the way more clearly by guiding the therapist while relating to a mental image of him. It is conceivable that this technique may be employed selectively for some patients without the use of a hypnotic setting.

The first time the method was employed, involving an interview with the therapist in fantasy, was on an occasion when a patient seemed to be seeking something within himself and when it was felt he might be assisted with certain pertinent inquiries and suggestions. Instead of working blindly, an attempt was made to have the patient ascribe appropriate comments or questions to the doctor. There is implied here some level of awareness on the part of the patient of what it is that he is seeking. He works with himself and uses the therapist as an extension of his own person. At the same time he incorporates certain objective attributes of the hypnoanalyst in terms of personal qualities, manner, and therapeutic approach.

If a patient has difficulty with visual techniques, he can deal with the fantasied material in terms of auditory features alone. Some patients may be able to have actual hypnotic auditory hallucinations but this is not essential. A patient may deal meaningfully with an imaginary conversation. An example of the latter is offered now. It should be kept in mind that the doctor is not, in fact speaking. What he is depicted as commenting here is what the patient is imagining him to be saying. The patient was a twenty-eight year old woman. She was in hypnoanalysis.

Doctor: You're in a mess. *Patient:* I'm not really in a mess. *Doctor:* You have no one but yourself to blame for your present lack of character. *Patient:* I'm trying—stupidly, I'm trying. *Doctor:* You know the facts. Work with them. *Patient:* I'm reaching. I'm going to. *Doctor:* You always say you're going to. You have lots of ideas and you don't carry them through. *Patient:* I know. *Doctor:* You disorganize in the sense of trying to do too much and you get too tense and irritated and act like a spoiled child because you're failing. You can't bear to fail. Anyone would fail in trying (to do too much). *Patient:* I know. . . . When I don't (accomplish what I want) I fume. Like when I try to defend myself against my husband's criticism when I'm not working. (She compared herself to someone else and he criticized her.) . . . He attacked me for conceit and I wasn't being conceited. I'm having the strangest sensation of something I've experienced before (before the onset of sleep at night). I feel in a great void, like being a flea in a great space. I feel like a great big area. I can't look at my plans realistically. *Doctor:* Are you really? *Patient:* Yes. I can indulge in fantasy . . . and see it as running away from responsibility . . . I know I'm not going to give up. I know if I can be more effective I wouldn't feel this present worthlessness. I have this feeling that my husband is unfair. And I suppose if I were he I would feel the same way. When he was my age he had learned his trade. So he has in his background subconsciously that women should (assume) responsibilities, should (derive) enough satisfaction from them. *Doctor:* That's a normal thing. *Patient:* Of course it's normal. I know he would like to help me. *Doctor:* Your husband? *Patient:* Yes. I think he would and he wouldn't. (The patient said her husband could not see how someone could arrive at the patient's age and not do something meaningful if he originally had the motivation) My set of circumstances were different . . . He had one asset, not to be taken lightly—the affection and warmth of his mother . . . Others (in my position) might be more productive. But I don't feel guilty . . . Maybe that's a self-satisfied way to feel . . . but I'm grateful you helped me to look at it that way. Instead of feeling guilty the way six other people would or would not have done something. I think you helped remove some of the guilt feeling and the worry . . . Even if it's a schizophrenic thing (her illness), I don't give a damn now. I'm not going to be a schizophrenic. If I was, I would have fallen into it a long time ago. If I found out I had such potentialities, I'm not going to be frightened by the word any more. If I can stop acting like a child and act like an adult seventy-five per cent of the time and see the twenty-five per cent for what it is! *Doctor:* You've got to do it. You've come along and I've helped you to see these things in a better light—perhaps not as much as you should—but you see things, and now it's your terms.

The following fantasy emerged during the next hypnoanalytic interview. As with the preceding material, the contents are given here without further comment. Careful examination of the material points readily to the multiplicity of interesting features evident in these data. Again, the doctor and his comments are products of the hypnotic fantasy.

Doctor: Why are you always a little afraid of hypnosis? *Patient:* I can't speak very well today. I'm just a little apprehensive. I'm apprehensive of everything. *Doctor:* How do you feel? *Patient:* I feel a little bit nervous. I have the sensation of dizziness. Of falling. Of being on a slant (motions with hand). *Doctor:* Where do we go from here? *Patient:* Slow work. I'm beginning to see the childishness of some of my habit patterns and I know it's just work from now on. *Doctor:* Did anything happen that you thought was odd this week? *Patient:* I was—I became aware of the amount of apprehension that I must have stored up as a child over some incident that was stupid. I would say I haven't acquired what I'd call courage—the see it through or ride with the punches approaches, rather than the stopping through fear immediately on approaching something— the slight bravo of go ahead, see what happens—what you might call curiosity . . . I feel stupid—a little unfamiliar with myself . . . I feel I'm on an awful slant. Would this slant mean that I'm not yet—that I'm working towards—that I'm on it until I feel at peace with myself? *Doctor:* It could. *Patient:* It's not frightening any more. It used to be. It's not the most desirable feeling. I felt it (some time ago) and it frightened me. I feel it now. It's a sensation you feel and perhaps it's telling you something—that you're not at home with yourself or at peace with yourself . . . You know now it's possible to be at peace with yourself. *Doctor:* Yes. I've told you it's possible. Perhaps you're beginning to accept it . . . *Patient:* Perhaps not whole heartedly . . . I know I'm compelled to believe it if I'm going to have enough security to go on . . . I don't want to quit. There's really nothing more to say. It's where I stand today. I believe you. Not the old believe you where I had a basic disbelief . . . I must not pretend . . . It's not a joyous position but not an unhappy position at this point. You can't visualize it but I know that you can only get better . . . and that it is possible, but not probable that I'll get worse. It's possible and probable that I'll get better. In the past I'd have a certain urgency and question you—"What can I do now?" —and it was a question of just keep working! . . . I'd ask—"Tell me to do something"—something on that level . . . This week I've been (distracted). There isn't any kind of agitation—a complacency, to go along and take the things that come up . . . to question real feelings about things. I'm sort of in the position of waiting. Not waiting in the sense of avoiding things—waiting to see what I learn as I function—not waiting to get better without doing anything or trying anything. I've had a . . . more affectionate attitude about sex this week . . . This week I felt two sensations simultaneously— feeling abstracted and feeling normal . . . both operating at the same time—not like previously—feeling a cold tomato one day and affectionate the next . . . I wasn't terribly surprised because I've realized slowly how contradictory my feelings have been . . . I felt it was healthy to experience two so contradictory things at once . . . I'm becoming healthier if I can stand to accept them together . . .

I have indicated that there are many aspects of these productions which can be examined in considerable detail. Only one will be touched on here. As the fantasy developed it seemed that the therapist in fantasy was applying pressure to the patient greater than what was believed to be so in fact. Despite this appearance of exaggeration, it prompted me to review my contacts with the patient in order to reassess this theme. Even though the pressure that seemed to be present were not really existent, the fact that the patient presented it this way was important. Certainly there was no doubt that this patient was terribly severe with herself and projected this severity on to the therapist in fantasy. She seemed, however, to be asking the hypnoanalyst to take note of her feelings in this regard.

I am not sure just when the specific use of a therapist in fantasy is potentially helpful. I refer to the deliberate utilization of the fantasy by the patient in the hypnotic setting. The presence of this fantasy is often implied in connection with hypnoanalytic and related procedures even though no special reference is made to it during treatment. The issue of a fantasy of an interpersonal relationship is discussed almost invariably when dealing with hypnosis from clinical and theoretical points of view. Perhaps the measure of having the patient conduct such conversation will prove to be of greatest value when concerns about transference and countertransference in particular are to be investigated. This remains to be seen. With some exceptions, it is not possible to state that certain categories of illness will respond better to hypnoanalytic measures than will others because so much depends on the total personality functioning of patients, their psychological status at certain times, and the nature of the transference relationship between doctor and patient at particular moments in therapy. Similarly it is not possible to say that one particular technique within the framework of hypnoanalysis should be helpful invariably in certain categories of illness or with certain symptoms. The hypnoanalytic measure of the fantasy therapist and all other measures mentioned thus far must be evaluated in terms of suitability for the individual patient, the point in time when the judgment is to be made, and due regard for the patient's psychological position within the context of the total therapeutic regime as visualized by the hypnoanalyst. While it is helpful to offer generalizations, they are frequently misleading. An example is the often repeated claim that "the hypnotic state is peculiarly suited to overcome resistance" (52) when, as a matter of fact, its induction frequently leads to intensification of resistances. The intensification and its manifestations may indeed then lead to analysis of the elements involved, and it is this secondary measure that may facilitate progress if the patient is adaptable to the techniques brought into play for this purpose.

18. Spontaneous Regressions, Hypnoanalysis, and the Superego

When, during hypnosis, a patient regresses spontaneously to a significant time period and recaptures material that proves helpful to him, the regression is apparently a function to a certain extent of the basic involvement in hypnosis and in a sense one may think of the occurrence as overcoming of resistance. But the mechanisms involved are more complex in terms of the preparedness for the phenomenon, and this period of preparation may actually have involved temporary accentuation of resistances of various types necessitating careful utilization of hypnotic methods to deal with them gradually. If one focusses on the dramatic regression only, the impression of what had been transpiring would be misleading. A patient in his twenties, to illustrate, had experienced a number of fainting attacks (Schneck, 53). At one point in treatment he "spontaneously" regressed to a time period when something meaningful related to the fainting episodes had taken place. The fact is that he did not regress in this way by virtue of an hypnotic state having been induced at just any time. It was the importance of the hypnosis at a particular time following a build-up of earlier personality evaluations supplying a groundwork and framework for the meaningful regression to take place "spontaneously." Similar occurrences are noted in non-hypnotic treatment, of course, except for the peculiar behavioral attributes of the hypnotic regression experience. The potential advantages of the hypnotic setting in a case such as this tend to be focussed on the regression because it is easy to pinpoint and to discuss, and because it can be delineated more easily and concretely than the sum of the complex happenings that preceded it.

The patient now under discussion spontaneously regressed, during one of his hypnoanalytic sessions, to the age of eleven when he had an operation on his nose, apparently a submucous resection. He relived the events and was quite disturbed about them at the time. The central theme of the event and of the regression related to the psychological interplay between the patient and his mother. He had objected to the procedure but felt coerced by her. He cursed her while succumbing to her perssure. Feeling compelled to comply, with the feeling of being overpowered by her personality was evidently a significant factor in a series of fainting episodes. The common denominator was the mother's dominant, controlling, yet quiet and firm influence over him. There were ties to an identification of his wife with his mother and certain representations of the patient's passive, feminine leanings.

The hypnoanalytic work in this case furnished material that served to extend observations by others through methods that did not always involve hypnosis and in areas of general medical interest. It touched on an area discussed earlier by Guze, pertaining to anesthesia and instrumentation trauma (54). It was related to a review of several types of fainting such as vasodepressor syncope and hysterical syncope described by Barnes (55). It was connected with Fenichel's account of psychoanalytic formulations dealing with fainting in terms of blocking or decrease of ego functions (40). Fainting has been described as an archaic and primitive defense against overwhelming stimuli. In the process of regression there is a blocking of some perceptions, and in fainting there is a blocking of all perceptions. The present patient with the fainting episodes was contending with pressures on the part of his mother that were identified as gross attacks, and in some of his dreams the aggression toward him was symbolized in the extreme form of murderous intentions toward him by his mother. Various aspects of these issues had come into view directly or indirectly during the hypnoanalysis and prior to the spontaneous regression, that, in a sense, crystallized them in more dramatic fashion.

Spontaneous hypnotic regressions often revert to specific events delineating conflict themes. At times, however, the central point of interest and focus of the regression pertains not so much to an actual happening, but to earlier attitudes and feelings of the patient and the attitudes and feelings of others toward the patient whether they be fact or fantasy. A woman in her thirties was deeply involved in hypnosis almost routinely and tended often to regress spontaneously. During her hypnoanalysis there were such sessions when she reverted to childhood settings and would speak repetitiously in a fashion that made it difficult to determine whether her utterances represented things she had said or thought as a child, or statements that her mother and father had made to her at that time, or feelings and attitudes possessed by her parents and adopted and introjected by the patient herself. Difficult as it was to draw the line between what she said and what they said or what she believed they felt, it became clear that a fusion was present that delineated developmental aspects of the patient's superego functioning. The latter was harsh and critical in ways that were clearly involved in current difficulties. It was of interest that following some of these hypno-analytic sessions, when the amnesic fog could clear sufficiently for this patient to realize what she had said, she was at times still un-able to differentiate in her own mind what represented her own statements and what reflected the attitudes of her parents. It is obvious that the theme of regression is of considerable practical importance in hypnoanalytic work and indeed in hypnotherapy in general. It is also of theoretical importance within this field of en-deavor, and in its broader aspects in the range of general psycho-analytic experience and in other areas of healing endeavor as Menninger has stressed (57).

One would be mistaken to believe that as far as hypnoanalytic settings are concerned, a regression is followed on the part of the patient by a sense of achievement or, in some cases of therapeutic achievement, by a sense of relief. The nature of the reaction de-pends upon the psychological status of the patient at the time. He may be seemingly unconcerned about the events of the regression. He may misevaluate the nature of his experience. He may deny its importance. He may express anxiety, not necessarily in connection with the psychological content of the regressed phase, so to speak, but over the nature of the occurrence itself. An interesting example of an event, to which the patient reacted first with fright following which she eased significantly when evaluating its implications, is that of a spontaneous regression to an infant age level during self-hypnosis. The patient had not employed techniques for regression in the course of hypnoanalytic work and knew nothing about the phenomenon. The self-hypnosis was being used to further her analytic efforts. What she experienced in the spontaneous regres-sion was mainly an awareness of feeling-tones. She seemed to be lying supine. There were no leg movements. Hand and arm move-ments were random in type. She could not turn her body. All mo-tions were slight. There was no awareness of a sequence of thoughts. Later in hypnosis she analyzed her experience as indicative of infantile, dependent needs and wishes (Schneck, 58).

An evaluation of this occurrence in greater detail soon after it happened appeared to point to the fact that it was perhaps un-usual as a spontaneous event, and the level of functioning apparent in the regression was evidently approximately that of a four month old infant. I recall in this connection a similar experience during the hypnoanalysis òf a woman in her fifties. The infantile helplessness that appeared spontaneously carried with it the vague sensation of being carried in the arms of an adult. Both episodes were experienced without concurrent self-evaluation. Scrutiny of the happenings by the patients occurred afterwards as I have noted often to be true of meaningful regressions of this type.

19. Notions of Superficial and Deep Psychotherapy

The woman just described was phobic and anxiety-ridden. The lessening of her anxiety was not accompanied by any appearance of depression directly related to the alteration of the anxiety-depression balance that I discussed earlier. Another patient presented a mixture of anxiety and depression in his initial complaints. They had been present for several years. He was assisted over a span of thirty-eight sessions. There appeared to be fluctuations in the levels of the anxiety and depression as relief was gradually experienced, and he appeared to present more the type of relationship between the two that had to be assessed constantly as treatment progressed. A variety of measures were used in his hypnoanalysis. These included conversational exchange with and without hypnosis, free association as well, hypnotic visual imagery with special reference to scene visualization within the meaning of the term that I have described specifically, analysis of spontaneous sensory and motor phenomena, hypnotic recall of nocturnal dreams and completion of dreams not fully remembered, an assortment of posthypnotic suggestions aimed at enhancing therapeutic endeavors by the patient, and hypnotic suggestions from time to time intended to help the patient in mastering feelings of anxiety and depression. Among problems dealt with were his hostility toward his father, his fear of authority figures, competitive feelings toward other men as related to his conflicts and anxieties, conflicts between ambition and the wish to escape responsibilities, suicidal thoughts, and obsessive fears of harming his wife and children.

A point arose in connection with the discussion of this case when, in an addendum to it, the question was asked as to how this would be classified if one were to consider that a continuum exists from superficial to deep psychotherapy (Schneck, 59). I replied then as

I would still answer now. The treatment of this patient would be closer to the designation of deep psychotherapy. Yet such evaluations of depth are always a matter of opinion linked to prejudices of theoretical orientation and to views of orthodoxy and related concerns. In a sense the terms superficial and deep have essentially little meaning. They have no direct connection with relative degrees of ease or difficulties in management of therapy. Patients in deep psychotherapy or in analysis in one form or another within the usual terms of reference are often easier to treat than others who, within the same context, would be regarded as experiencing superficial psychotherapy. Thus, a hypnoanalyst may have an easier contact when attempting to help a patient over a period of time with evaluations of complex dynamics, interpretations, and transference—countertransference concerns than he may have with efforts aimed at alleviating as directly as possible a particular symptom of a patient, using hypnotherapeutic methods. And in his more circumscribed hypnotherapeutic approach for symptomatic relief he brings to the fore, one must realize, all his knowledge of, and experience with personality operations and fine points in the doctor-patient relationship of which not one word or note of interpretation may have been uttered.

20. Hypnotic Dreams and Scene Visualizations

I have referred to the use of hypnotic dreams and scene visualizations among the variety of techniques employed in hypnoanalysis. It might be surmised that more significant material can be derived through the use of dreams because, by implication, such material would be attended by greater distortions consistent with stronger resistances. This is, however, not necessarily so. In the case of a young woman, to use a simple example, the mere transposition of certain characteristics from one person to another within the context of everyday type settings, in the framework of hypnotic scene visualizations, permitted the clarification of a meaningful identification. This patient had hidden, incestuous longings toward her father which resulted in feelings of distaste and physical illness when in contact with him at times. Characteristics of a boyfriend as depicted in the hypnotic visualizations, namely slovenliness and teasing, were in fact the traits of her father under certain circum stances. They revealed themselves first when a dream was suggested and then when a scene visualization was suggested. The emerging imagery in both cases was characteristic of scene visualization (Schneck, 60). This is not uncommon. Sometimes when dreams are suggested, the emerging productions resemble simple everyday settings. And when scenes are suggested, more complex dream work may come into view. The product stemming from a suggestion of any type is, in clinical work, more important than the reason for its having conformed to one structural pattern or another. This holds true unless the nature of the structural pattern has diagnostic significance for the patient in question, with special reference to the therapeutic atmosphere rather than to his basic mode of functioning not directly related to the problems immediately at hand.

For another patient, conflict in connection with an incestuous theme emerged also in vivid fashion through hypnotic imagery. This young woman had a water phobia. Though an excellent swimmer, she avoided going into the water whenever possible. When she was to visualize a scene reflecting the first appearance of her fear, she could think only of a series of water dreams that she had had previously. Under such circumstances, the hypnotic setting can at times circumvent secondary material and move closer to the core of a problem. Here, she was told that she would now dream again only the most significant of these dreams. She started to do so, but then found that her thoughts switched to an actual occurrence in which she was swept along by a strong current. These thoughts led to another dream that preceded this happening, and in it an unidentified person was drowning. With the use of visual imagery she was brought to an identification of the individual who turned out to be her father. Anxiety was stirred up, as a result, in connection with the underlying theme of her death wishes toward him. The disappearance of the phobia entailed, shortly thereafter, clarification of important connecting links. There was an identification, as with the preceding patient, of a boyfriend with her father. There was an actual event linking the boyfriend with a water setting when, after an argument, he left the patient and swam out and away from her. She proceeded elsewhere to swim far out into the ocean in a conscious suicidal gesture, only to change her mind when allegedly thinking of the distress this act would cause her parents. There was also involved in the water phobia the symbolic association of a large body of water with her mother in terms of a powerful, overwhelming, controlling force with which she had to contend (Schneck, 61).

21. Aspects of Denial, Hypnotic Paralysis, and Sleep Paralysis

This patient would be quite involved emotionally in her hypnoanalytic sessions almost routinely. From time to time she would manifest a phenomenon sufficiently interesting to be stressed now. During a session she would ask that the hypnosis be terminated. On inquiry, she would respond that the reason for the request was based on the absence of meaningful thoughts. She would claim that ideas occurring to her were unimportant, or she would say that her mind was completely blank. It was discovered that at such times especially, she would be on the verge of bringing to awareness highly significant data, and her allegations were an effort to re-enforce repression. Concurrently she would be seen often to breathe deeply in keeping with her emotion, and to struggle bodily in an attempt to break through the hypnosis even though she was not told that she would be unable to achieve this. When encouraged to continue verbalizing, the significant, repressed data would emerge. At the height of her reaction she would in effect be paralyzed. Depending on its phase, she might or might not be able to talk. She would experience considerable anxiety. She would be able to verbalize when the anxiety subsided a bit. The feeling of patients that they are unable to move at all is not unusual. At times such patients experience some anxiety, though generally not as profound as in the aforementioned patient. They may refer to the inability to move during the hypnosis session itself, or they may tell of it after termination. With varying motivations, they may claim during the hypnosis that they can move if they wished to do so, only to find at times that they cannot when they actually attempt it.

The marked reaction of the woman with the episodes of anxiety and inability to move is reminiscent of episodes of sleep paralysis that I have discussed in a series of publications, only to one of which I make reference now (Schneck, 62). Sleep paralysis occurs on falling off to sleep or waking from it. Some patients have hallucinatory experiences with it and these are, of course, dynamically pertinent as would be the case with the repressed thoughts and imagery in the hypnoanalytic sessions under discussion now. I have suspected that in certain patients with sleep paralysis, the theme of conflict over passive and aggressive strivings plays a role in the episodes and is reflected in them. This holds true, I should say, for the woman mentioned above and in similar cases. Sleep paralysis phenomena vary in frequency and intensity, and these parallel the occurrences of similar phenomena in hypnosis. The apparent connection between the two situations is worth noting.

22. Denial of Hypnosis, Alleged Simulation of Hypnosis, and the Concept of Pseudo-malingering

The same patient would ask often to be permitted to leave the couch on which she was lying in order to sit again in the chair near the desk. Making the request would be necessary for her at such times because in fact, as noted above, she would find herself unable to move. Despite this, when asked the reason for her request, she would claim that she was not in hypnosis at all. Again, it was discovered at such times that not only was she involved in the hypnosis, but she was approaching dynamically significant and frequently highly cathected material that forces of repression were no longer able to keep satisfactorily in check. Many patients, in order to minimize the dynamic significance of the hypnotic relationship with its transference implications for them, claim that they are not in hypnosis or that the actions they manifested when supposedly entering hypnosis were really of no consequence, did not indicate the existence of a hypnotic state, and could be readily simulated by them without difficulty. When they are permitted to demonstrate this, they show many subtle phenomena in eye movements, lid characteristics, and cogwheel movements in hand levitation that are so peculiar to subjects moving into hypnosis. Intervention by the hypnoanalyst at points during the alleged demonstration reveal the existence of the hypnotic contact when the patients presumably believe they are falsifying it. These occurrences are a reminder of certain events that I have reported and discussed under the heading of pseudo-malingering (Schneck, 63).

I have described pseudo-malingering as occurrences in which patients deliberately feign psychological symptoms only to find afterwards that they had, in fact, without being consciously aware of it at the time, suffered the very distress they had believed they were falsifying. The phenomenon seems to reflect a self-exclusion component of ego functioning. For such patients, the maneuver is an emergency device to maintain the integrity of the ego. This would apply also, I should say, to the hypnotic settings when patients, fearing disruptions of ego functioning and control, find it necessary to believe that they are simulating the very situations in which they are in fact participating and which they are experiencing. The patients with anxiety and depression that I discussed elsewhere as pseudo-malingerers attempted to deny illness by the expedient of claiming such illness. The hypnotic patients say in effect —I shall show myself that I am not experiencing hypnosis by proving that I can falsely duplicate such experience. In the effort to duplicate it, however, they are only confirming that they are indeed experiencing it. When I reported on pseudo-malingering I said that it is probably far more widespread and its characteristics more subtle than indicated by the patients then presented. I believe some of the hypnoanalytic settings confirm this point in at least this one additional area.

23. Hypnoanalysis and Phobic Symptomatology

As I review my own experience, I believe it would be fair to say that overcoming phobic reactions in patients is accomplished more readily when they are dealt with during the course of hypnoanalysis as one of many problems, in contrast to sharp stress on severe phobias presented as the main reason for treatment itself. The water phobia discussed earlier serves as one example. It entailed no sense of urgency at the initiation of treatment. Another example is that of a cat phobia in a patient who dealt with it during her hypnoanalysis in a manner which differed from that of the aforementioned patient (Schneck, 61). Her emotional reactions during the investigation were less intense. She showed more of a tendency to evaluate her thoughts and feelings quietly as they appeared. Her phobia reflected her ambivalence toward her mother. The cat with the tail fit the concept of the phallic mother. Her fear of cats dated back as far as she could remember into her childhood years. Notions about the cat as an unpredictable, untrustworthy, aggressive animal found a parallel in her image of a hostile female figure. This patient identified herself in part with the phallic features of her mother as she herself assumed more and more the masculine identification which she believed appealed to her father. The cat phobia embodied her fear of her mother's hostility and entailed at the same time a projection of her own hostility and her fear of this as well.

This patient saw in her husband certain qualities that linked him with her mother. Essentially, she saw in him the characteristics implying a feminine identification. She had started treatment because of marital difficulties. For her, the best relationship in terms of a gratifying experience with him was the sexual relationship in which her complex needs and mixed identifications permitted use of this particular outlet better than others. Under circumstances of special stress or difficulty with him, she could substitute others in her fantasies during the relationship with her husband and achieve physical and at times psychological gratification in this way as well. She would at times substitute the hypnoanalyst in this fashion and the transference elements found expression at one point in the hypnotic setting through her wish to lie on her side during induction, bringing him into view, with her coquettish manner reflecting her unmistakable seductive intent.

24. The Past and the Present

Hypnotic procedures so often bring to mind for many the idea, as I have expressed on a number of occasions, of the search for specific, early events that might have influenced strongly the problems of adult life. This early psychoanalytic theme still affects the interests and techniques of some hypnoanalysts and many psychoanalysts. Increasingly, however, on the basis of the accumulating experiences of many therapists or the guidance of a few, the importance of stress on more recent happenings as well as on the past has come in for a more meaningful share of attention. Alexander has reenforced this point by saying that regressions to pre-traumatic or pre-conflictual periods can offer good opportunities in personality research, but that they are not valuable therapeutically (64). Furthermore, a patient may regress in his free associations to early infantile data as a way of evading essential pathogenic conflicts Much time can be wasted in this evasion and if the therapist participates there is mutual self-deception.

The stress on early years has had such impact on the psychologically minded public that many patients show fierce determination to pursue this "deep material" epitomized in early experiences to the point of scornful unconcern with anything else and a regarding of all else as "superficial."

A thirty year old patient suffering from impotence and the anxiety related to exposure to sexual opportunities was able, in his hypnoanalysis, to connect his problem in part to the nature of his relationship with his mother. She was a hovering, controlling person whom he had not heretofore recognized as such, and his ideas about her attitudes toward him resulted in feelings of guilt of an intensity he had not realized heretofore. It was only after he had dealt with a multiplicity of adolescent and adult issues in this area, and had established a meaningful and almost completely normal relationship with one woman in particular, that he experienced during a series of hypnosis sessions a feeling that some special theme seemed about to come to consciousness although it had persisted in eluding him. Finally, he recalled an event when he was five years old. His mother had been bathing him. She played with his penis and jokingly threatened to bite it off. I suspect that had this memory been forced to the surface, so to speak, in a premature fashion, its significance might have been essentially isolated and it would have had little or no influence on his overcoming the impotence problem. For the latter there was implicated a broader array of themes within the framework of personal interrelationships that had to be examined first. When the early memory emerged in hypnosis it served as a confirmation and extension of important points in his problem. It did not appear as a sudden flash of enlightenment.

25. Hypnosis-homosexuality Equations

It is of interest to compare this patient, with his sexual difficulties, to another who from time to time would comment about his sexual functioning and take pride in his prowess. While in treatment he knew about the writer's work with hypnoanalysis but was not acquainted with the details. He had wondered several times about asking for such treatment but had been unable to get himself to do so. Then he had a dream in which a snake was being charmed by a snake charmer who was wearing a turban. Later in his dream the patient found himself holding a chair which he used to defend himself against the snake. His associations to the snake were penis and himself. The snake charmer led to associations of doctor and to me. The snake was being hypnotized and in the dream this represented the patient being hypnotized by the therapist. The sexual symbolism pointed to a homosexual situation. Hypnosis was equated in this dream with homosexuality. The defense against the snake was interpreted by the patient as his attempt to defend himself against latent homosexual impulses. It reflected his homosexual conflict (Schneck, 65).

Another patient had a dream in which a woman was lying on a cot. She was dead. He made a hypnosis-death equation and a hypnosis-homosexuality identification. His associations pointed to the cot as the analytic couch. He identified himself with the woman. He concluded that the hypnotic relationship was a homosexual one for him. He felt passive and feminine in hypnosis despite his activity in the hypnoanalytic work. He identified the hypnoanalyst with his father. The transference relationship incorporated considerable feelings of hostility on his part.

Still another patient equated the hypnotic relationship with homosexuality during an initial interview. He did not verbalize his feelings, suppressed them in fact, and later repressed for a time his awareness of this identification until he was able eventually to permit it to reach a level of awareness again. The identification of hypnosis and homosexuality was found to relate in part to early school experiences when there was homosexual play among the youngsters and at the same time some attempts by a few of the boys to hypnotize others. Homosexuality became identified in the mind of this patient as an activity deserving punishment by death, and hypnosis was feared as a means by which death dealing suggestions could be given. Punishment was identified with parent and therapist and self-punitive needs were expressed in this case through identifications by the patient with both parent and hypnoanalyst.

26. Rapid Investigations, Premature Termination of Treatment, and Hypnotic Control

Regarding the issue of transference and identifications, it has been my experience that meaningful clarification of these issues can be achieved often for patients who are capable of working with automatic writing (Schneck, 66). I discussed one such case where the investigation was accomplished early in treatment. It was embarked on when the patient, during hypnosis and with her eyes open, would persistently avoid looking directly at the therapist. Automatic writing revealed an association between the therapist and another individual with whom a friend of the patient had had sexual relations. The patient herself had double dated with this friend and also had had extramarital sexual contacts. The therapeutic measures served to enlighten us regarding the nature of her defenses against sexual thoughts, associations, and impulses. There is a risk, however, in early clarification of highly charged preconscious and unconscious material, because its appearance can result in premature termination of treatment. I have had such experiences based on what I should regard as my own errors and I realize too that so often one is confronted with the dilemma of taking such a risk or not taking it when under persistent pressure by patients for rapid alleviation of distress.

An association to this now is the case of a middle aged man with an impotence problem, caught in the immediate demands of a sexual relationship and attempting to overcome his difficulty as rapidly and expeditiously as possible. Hypnoanalytic measures with particular reference to automatic writing began to reveal a role that his mother was playing in his difficulties. With the appearance of this theme, he terminated treatment. It would be a mistake to believe that invariably the patient can be protected by management of hypnotic sessions in such a way as to preclude conscious awareness by the patient of material elicited, as may be the case in automatic writing by attempting to prevent the patient from recognizing the nature of his productions. The material is organized or reorganized unconsciously by the patient and this is indeed sufficient at times to lead to the patient's retreat even though he does not consciously recognize the nature of his problem. He knows it unconsciously so to speak, but even on that level one might say he knows it too well, with the concurrent risk of its erupting into consciousness before he is prepared to handle it. He sees no choice but to discontinue treatment and easily furnishes some rationalization for taking this step.

The direction that certain procedures take and their dynamic implications are highlighted in the case of a patient in hypnoanalysys for whom, at one point, focus was centered on the theme of vocational choice. I had been involved prior to that in studies dealing with hypnosis and vocational interests, and the scene visualization technique had been used in these explorations (Kline and Schneck, 67). The present patient's responses to instructions regarding images to be evoked showed that when attempts were made to fathom unconscious preferences in the realm of vocational interests, the image products were indeed not simple at all. A patient involved in an earlier study was able to demonstrate simple responses such as "I'm painting a picture," "I'm reading a story—broadcasting," "I see myself giving Rorschach tests." In contrast to her scenes, this patient revealed imagery with a dream-like quality and the productions were often distantly related to the instructions as far as manifest elements were concerned. The latent content derived from his personality problems and the transference relationship. Attempts to simplify the imagery by repetition of simple instructions and defining the goal specifically were unsuccessful. It must be realized, therefore, that in the hypnotic setting the element of control, in terms of direction taken by the patient in keeping with deep inner psychological needs, is very much dependent upon his requirements at the time (Schneck, 68). The notion of the powerful, controlling role of the hypnotist, or for our current concerns the hypnotherapist or hypnoanalyst, tends to be greatly exaggerated in so far as its fulfillment is concerned. I have in mind specifically the notion of his firm mastery through technical maneuvers aimed at eliciting specific responses.

27. Dynamics of Interest in Hypnosis

The power role and omnipotent strivings of the hypnotist are, perhaps, stressed most when reference is made to his personal needs in the hypnotic relationship. This skims the surface and often is not helpful in any serious attempt to understand what is involved in this choice of activity by any one individual. Similar personal needs may apply of course to other avenues of operation whether the person involved be an internist, surgeon, or psychoanalyst. I have had occasion to treat a number of professional people included among whom were individuals either interested in the use of hypnosis or actually employing hypnotic methods in their own work. At this point there is nothing remarkable to report regarding hypnotizability, methods of utilizing the hypnotic setting, or dynamics of their concern with hypnosis. I think it may be of interest, however, to comment on a patient who functioned as an amateur hypnotist because he was studied fairly extensively in the course of a hypnoanalysis and his cooperativeness permitted elicitation of considerable material relating to the significance of the hypnosis issue for him.

The hypnosis concern for this patient may be summarized as follows. He connected the theme of hypnosis with the broader field of mental functioning and mental health. A knowledge of hypnosis symbolized, within the context of his own problems, intellectual accomplishment. This specifically was indentified with power. He felt himself related through his hypnosis activities with scientific investigators in this area and this signified a link with authority. His low level of self-esteem was thus elevated. He desired respect and appreciation from parents and siblings as well as others, and identifying himself with authority and intellectual concerns helped to satisfy this need. Admiration would be increased if the practical return of financial gain could also be obtained in this way. His identification with authority incorporated competitive feelings toward his father specifically. Praise by subjects and members of an audience was identified by him with praise from his mother. He was in fact acting out oedipal strivings.

Success with hypnosis meant that this patient was selling his subject. It was noteworthy for him because he was selling an often criticized product. His success would compensate for deficiencies of salesmanship in other areas. Feeling deficient in his interpersonal relations, this patient believed he could achieve closer contact with people as members of demonstration groups as well as individual subjects. They would substitute for goals he had difficulty in attaining. His hypnotic relationships were sexually colored and as a result he attempted to satisfy in fantasy the shortcomings he felt because of his sexual immaturity. He tried to advance a sense of increasing maturity in his attention to psychological literature through his hypnotic interests.

As a hypnotist, this patient pictured himself as a healer. He expressed interest in hypnosis as a healing device and had fantasies involving identifications with Jesus as psychologist and hypnotic healer. In the transference relationship during the hypnoanalysis, he identified himself with the therapist as authority. He expressed and satisfied competitive urges in this relationship. He exercised needs to control in his therapeutic contact. He was interested in self-hypnosis and obtained a sense of achievement when employing it. He obtained satisfactions vicariously through the accomplishments of his hypnotic subjects. His hypnosis activities were exhibitionistic, and his exhibitionism was undoubtedly a motivating element in his request for hypnoanalysis. It supplemented his search for relief from anxiety, depression, and sexual inadequacy (Schneck, 71).

28. Hypnoanalysis and Psychoanalysis

Lerner compared psychoanalysis and hypnoanalysis in his writings, covering a number of points such as time elements and areas of application. He considers hypnoanalysis the treatment of choice for the neuroses, psychosomatic problems and some psychoses without denying the value of psychoanalysis in some cases (14). This brings up an issue which cannot be answered definitely in my opinion. Resistances to the use of hypnosis are present in patients who seek hypnoanalysis of their own volition. Many more patients would probably be sharply resistant if hypnoanalysis were recommended as the first treatment of choice. Unless a patient were, at present, to seek it specifically, it would probably be more expedient to initiate treatment without hypnosis while building up a favorable doctor-patient relationship. If hypnoanalysis can become more of an integral part of psychiatric therapies in general so that prospective patients would be quite aware of its presence and implications, its consideration as a first choice procedure could be entertained more readily. It has, I believe, not reached this point as yet. If one were to disregard this practical drawback, it would be reasonable to claim that in many cases hypnoanalysis, because of what it has potentially to offer, may well be regarded as a favored approach provided that dogmatic assertions pertaining to its definite superiority be avoided in any generalizations as to its place in psychotherapy.

There is no one treatment approach or theoretical orientation that can legitimately be proclaimed the most desirable.

Any meaningful comparison between hypnoanalysis and psychoanalysis is out of the question for authors of virtually all writings dealing essentially with conventional psychoanalytic issues including neo-Freudian views and methods. A basic reason for this is their lack of understanding of fundamental premises in hypnoanalysis, no less the absence of experience. But beyond this is the remarkable lack of knowledge pertaining to fundamentals of hypnosis, no less hypnoanalysis. The level of understanding and knowledge among professional people is often that of the general public, and frequently below that level when emotional resistances have precluded curiosity about, and absorption of simple factual data. One simple example of misunderstanding is a reference to hypnosis by Thompson in her discussion of the evolution and development of psychoanalysis (15). When mentioning Freud's coming upon free association as a therapeutic technique, she added it possessed an advantage over hypnosis in that the patient remained conscious, without requiring the need to be informed later of what had taken place. Here are two common misconceptions, generally encountered among layman and those professionals who frequently offer authoritative pronouncements on hypnosis without having become acquainted with elementary facts. The majority of patients do not spontaneously experience posthypnotic amnesia so that they do not have to be told anything about content of the sessions. Furthermore, patients in hypnosis are not unconscious, a claim which in itself is rather odd for anyone aware of Freud's early work with hypnosis.

A few years ago, Wolff published a book of interviews with representatives of various schools of psychotherapy (16). I was able at that time, when contributing to it, to express some of my views on hypnotherapy and hypnoanalysis. Included among questions pertaining to technique and theory were one or more dealing with hypnosis regardless of the school of thought represented by the interviewee, or of his therapeutic and theoretical preferences. In looking through the volume it is possible to gain a sampling of opinions and attitudes by a number of people with established reputations whether or not they have had little or no experience with hypnosis.

Rado, for example, in giving his opinion about hypnosis, lauded its possibilities in emergency treatment and commented too that hypnosis was not yet understood sufficiently. The latter claim can, I should say, apply to every aspect of psychotherapy in use today. Generally the statement is made that there is no adequate theory of hypnosis. This is most peculiar again because the same is true for many areas of scientific investigation and empirical advances are surely acceptable in practical terms when legitimately assessed, regardless of the presence or absence of supporting theoretical structures. In recent years there have been put forward, in fact, a number of theoretical ideas, in relation to hypnosis, that give it solid scientific investment on a level equal to, or superior to other areas of medical and scientific concern.

Spitz (18) expressed the opinion that hypnosis was useful in conjunction with psychoanalytically oriented therapy but not with psychoanalysis. Even more now than at the time the statement was made, this claim has become a matter of semantics. It has become increasingly evident that a spectrum of procedures within a psycho-analytic framework must be given serious consideration in any assessment of psychoanalysis. The acceptance of therapeutic efforts that take into consideration the dynamic unconscious, resistance and transference is certainly widespread. Alterations in technique are common in practice, regardless of what is placed in print by the practioners themselves.

A widely held opinion was offered by Oberndorf (19). It does not hold true for hypnosis in its recent developments, nor did it necessarily apply in all cases when the claim was originally made. He spoke of an essential defect in hypnosis that existed when Freud abandoned it and that has not been overcome. This is the gap be-tween conscious memory and revelations under hypnosis. He said that discoveries under hypnosis were seldom integrated into the personality so as to become a continuous force for altered conduct. These claims need not be true in any form of hypnotherapy. Whether they are or are not true would depend on the personalities of the patients and the clinical measures employed by therapists. The assertions are quite untrue for hypnoanalysis as the present volume attests.

In line with the points just mentioned, the opinions of Lorand (20) are negated by experience of the past few decades. Hypnosis is not only a symptom therapy that does not touch the core of the neurosis. Even if it were an especially effective symptom therapy it would have a meaningful contribution to offer because difficulties in symptom alleviation are so widespread in more traditional psychoanalytic settings. The additional point that he made about the patient's having to be educated about his unconscious problems following hypnosis has no relation whatever to hypnoanalysis and need have no relation to other forms of hypnotherapy. Furthermore, it happens so often that patients seeking hypnoanalysis, when referring to previous psychoanalytic treatment, say that they have been given to understand certain problems are at the core of their difficulties not because they have come to see this for themselves, but because their analysts have told them it is so.

One more opinion may be cited to bring this series to a close. Horney (21) stated that hypnosis runs counter to the principle of the patient's active participation in his own development. This view is completely contradicted by the enormous quantity of clinical and experimental studies of the past few decades. It can be set aside as an indication of lack of familiarity with any of the significant work in this field.

It is, perhaps, surprising that there was no specific stress, in all of these opinions, on transference issues. To do so, however, would have required more direct contact with, and familiarity with hypnotherapeutic settings. Watkins (22) claimed at one point that difficulties in resolving transference ties in psychoanalysis were related to the existence of the analyst as an ever present reality figure, whereas in hypnoanalysis the transferences are largely to projected fantasies and less directly toward the "ink blot of the analyst." This, he felt, lessened the risk of an undissolved transference neurosis. Whether or not one agrees with this point of view, it is my impression that transference difficulties appear less in hypnoanalytic work. I think it relates to the greater autonomy in functioning that is present for the patient in hypnoanalysis, contrary to what many may surmise without the benefit of such clinical experience.

When the aforementioned views were expressed by Watkins, other aspects of his discussion dealt with less time required for hypnoanalysis as contrasted with traditional psychoanalysis. At a later date, Harold Lindner (23) was discussing this point concerning time when he commented that the combination of psychoanalysis and hypnosis supplied the opportunity for decreasing the length of treatment. He added, however, that the claim may be questionable because of recent developments in psychoanalytic theory with greater emphasis on ego psychology and ego analysis and the analysis of defense mechanisms. He said these preclude the cursory attention given them by the hypnoanalyst whose view of psychoanalysis is relatively fixed to its earlier developmental stages. I might note again that hypnoanalysis always supplies the possibility of saving time although it has been my impression that the time factor has been stressed unduly. Some hypnoanalysts are undoubtedly fixated at earlier developmental stages of psychoanalysis in theoretical approach and technique, in accordance with Harold Lindner's claim. But they need not be, and developments in ego psychology and ego analysis are not inconsistent with current operations and potentials in hypnoanalysis. This view is evident if not by direct statement, then by implication in recent publications on hypnoanalysis. I do not think Harold Lindner implied that concurrent developments in these areas of investigation would prevent satisfactory merging of new therapeutic measures and theoretical constructions.

Gill and Brenman (24) have stated that they have attempted to limit their use of the term "hypnoanalysis" to a form of psychotherapy that seeks to deal systematically with resistance and transference. Hypnotic methods are used as adjuvants. They add, however, that they believe the term "hypnotherapy" is misleading and suggest it be abandoned. Furthermore they consider the term "hypnoanalysis" to be sufficiently lacking in specificity as to be regarded as useless. Hypnosis can be employed to a minimal degree in psychoanalytic therapy from time to time, and it may be used actively by incorporating various specialized techniques. Dismissal of the term "hypnoanalysis" does not seem warranted on the basis of the claims they made if one sees this as an imperative, dogmatic assertion. If one simply chooses to avoid the term through personal preference, even though hypnotic methods have played a significant role in an analysis, this can be accepted as the analyst's choice. But words do not alter the events and one may be faced only with a quibble over semantics. One may question the necessity for using the term "psychoanalysis" in lieu of "psychoanalytic psychotherapy" or the use of either in lieu of the more broadly based "psychotherapy."

My view of hypnoanalysis as part of psychoanalysis as discussed at length up to this point was suggested by implication and succinctly when I had occasion to comment on its failures as well as its successes. I said that, in general, the elements contributing to its failures are similar to those encountered in the various forms and modifications of psychoanalytic therapy (Schneck, 25). A few reasons for special difficulties can be highlighted. They consist of conflict in some patients over submission and control problems that hypnosis presents for them. For others there is unusual distress stemming from sexualization of the hypnotic transference. At times anxiety and resistances are too strongly mobilized as a result of uncontrolled uprooting of highly charged unconscious material. Countertransference reactions that are poorly understood and dealt with may interfere with proper management of treatment. With its successes and despite its failures, we can say, on the basis of accumulating experience, that hypnoanalysis is meaningful and helpful and continues to develop and grow as a therapeutic adjunct and as a measure for exploring personality functioning.

References

1. Lindner, R. M.: Hypnoanalysis in a case of hysterical somnambulism. *Psychoanal. Rev.*, *32:*325, 1945.
2. Paley, A.: Hypnotherapy in the treatment of alcoholism. *Bull. Menninger Clin.*, *16:*14, 1952.
3. Wolberg, L. R.: A mechanism of hysteria elucidated during hypnoanalysis. *Psychoanal. Quart.*, *14:*no. 4, 1945.
4. Wolberg, L. R.: *Hypnoanalysis*. New York, Grune and Stratton, 1945.
5. Freytag, F. F.: *The Hypnoanalysis of an Anxiety Hysteria*. New York, Julian Press, 1959.
6. Watkins, J. G. *Hypnotherapy of War Neuroses*. New York, Ronald Press, 1949.
7. Schneck, J. M.: Hidden determinants in deceptive requests for hypnoanalysis. *Int. J. Clin. Exp. Hyp.*, *9:*261, 1961.
8. Klemperer, E.: Projective phenomena in hypnoanalysis. *Int. J. Clin. Exp. Hyp.*, *10:*127, 1962.
9. Klemperer, E.: Primary object-relationships as revealed in hypnoanalysis. *Int. J. Clin. Exp. Hyp.*, *9:*3, 1961.

10. Klemperer, E.: "Shortest distance" therapy in hypnoanalysis. *Int. J. Clin. Exp. Hyp.*, *9:*63, 1961.

11. Klemperer, E.: Social anxiety, early sexual and aggressive theories as revealed through hypnoanalysis. *Psychoanal. Rev.*, *44:*81, 1957.

12. Lerner, M.: Hipnoanálisis de los Mecanismos Inconscientes de Resistencia a la Curación. *Acta Hipnologica Latino-americana*, *2:*339, 1961.

13. Lerner, M.: Hipnoanálisis del Fenómeno de Desdoblamiento en una Psicosis Alucinatoria. *Acta Neuropsiquiat. Argent.*, *6:*72, 1960.

14. Lerner, M.: Psicoanálisis e Hipnoanálisis. *Acta Neuropsiquiat. Argent.*, *7:*283, 1961.

15. Thompson, C.: *Psychoanalysis: Evolution and Development.* New York, Hermitage House, 1950.

16. Wolff, W.: *Contemporary Psychotherapists Examine Themselves.* Springfied, Ill., Thomas, 1956.

17. Rado, S.: Scientific psychotherapy. See reference 16.

18. Spitz, R. A.; Psychoanalysis. See reference 16.

19. Oberndorf, C. P.: Liberal psychoanalysis. See reference 16.

20. Lorand, S.: Brief psychotherapy. See reference 16.

21. Horney, K.: Evolutionary psychotherapy. See reference 16.

22. Watkins, J. G.: Projective hypnoanalysis, in Le Cron, L. M.: *Experimental Hypnosis.* New York, Macmillan, 1952.

23. Lindner, H.: Hypnoanalysis: methods and techniques, in Dorcus, R. M.: *Hypnosis and Its Therapeutic Applications.* New York, Blakiston Division, McGraw Hill, 1956.

24. Gill, M. M., and Brenman, M.: *Hypnosis and Related States.* New York, International University Press, 1959.

25. Schneck, J. M.: Hypnoanalysis. *Int. J. Clin. Exp. Hyp.*, *10:*1, 1962.

26. Raginsky, B. B.: Sensory hypnoplasty with case illustrations. *Int. J. Clin. Exp. Hyp.*, *10:*205, 1962.

27. Watkins, J. G.: The hypnoanalytic treatment of a case of impotence. *J. Clin. Psychopath.*, *8:*453, 1947.

28. Schneck, J. M.: Hypnosis-death and hypnosis-rebirth concepts in relation to hypnosis theory. *J. Clin. Exp. Hyp.*, *3:*40, 1955.

29. Schneck, J. M.: Hypnotherapy in a case of claustrophobia and its implications for psychotherapy in general. *J. Clin. Exp. Hyp.*, *2:*251, 1954.

30. Schneck, J. M.: Luckenschadel in a patient with amnesia amenable to hypnotherapy: a personality study. *J. Nerv. Ment. Dis.*, *104:*249, 1946.

31. Schneck, J. M.: The divided personality: a case study aided by hypnosis. *J. Clin. Exp. Hyp.*, *2:*220, 1954.

32. Schneck, J. M.: Hypnoanalytic elucidation of motivation and goal in relation to psychotherapy. *Dis. Nerv. Syst.*, *16:*173, 1955.

33. Schneck, J. M.: Hypnoanalytic therapy with case illustrations. *Amer. J. Psychother.*, *10:*536, 1956.

34. Whitman, R. Kramer, M., and Baldridge, B.: Which dream does the patient tell? *Arch. Gen. Psychiat.*, *8:*277, 1963.

35. Eysenck, H. J.: Behavior therapy, spontaneous remission and transference in neurotics. *Amer. J. Psychiat.*, *119:*867, 1963.

36. Eysenck, H. J., Ed.: *Handbook of Abnormal Psychology.* New York, Basic Books, 1960.

37. Schneck, J. M.: Micropsia. *Amer. J. Psychiat.*, *118:*232, 1961.

38. Freud, S.: Fausse Reconnaissance (Déjà Raconté) in psychoanalytic treatment (1913), in *Collected Papers.* London, Hogarth, 1924.

39. Freud, S.: A disturbance of memory on the acropolis (1936), in *Collected Papers.* London, Hogarth, 1950.

40. Fenichel, O.: *The Psychoanalytic Theory of Neurosis.* New York, Norton, 1952.

41. Schneck, J. M.: A contribution to the analysis of déjà vu. *J. Nerv. Ment. Dis.*, *132:*91, 1961.

42. Schneck, J. M.: Dreams and déjà vu. *Psychosomatics*, *5:*116, 1964.

43. Schneck, J. M.: Automatic writing under hypnosis. *Brit. J. Med. Hyp.*, *Autumn:*1, 1954.

44. Stillerman, B.: The management in analytic hypnotherapy of the psychodynamic reaction to the induction of hypnosis. *J. Clin. Exp. Hyp.*, *5:*3, 1957.

45. Schneck, J. M.: Hypnoanalytic study of a patient with extrasystoles. *J. Clin. Exp. Hyp.*, *1:*11, 1953.

46. Dunbar, H. F.: *Emotions and Bodily Changes.* New York, Columbia University Press, 1938.

47. Bennett, L. L., and Scott, N. E.: The production of electrocardiographic abnormalities by suggestion under hypnosis. *Amer. Practitioner*, *4:*189, 1949.

48. Bowers, M. K., Berkowitz, B., and Brecher, S.: Hypnosis in severely dependent states. *J. Clin. Exp. Hyp.*, *2:*2, 1954.

49. Schneck, J. M.: A hypnoanalytic investigation of psychogenic dyspnea with the use of induced auditory hallucinations and special additional hypnotic techniques. *J. Clin. Exp. Hyp.*, *2:*80, 1954.

50. Watkins, J. G.: Trance and transference: *J. Clin. Exp. Hyp.*, *2:*284 1954.

51. Schneck, J. M.: Hypnotic interviews with the therapist in fantasy. *J. Clin. Exp. Hyp.*, *3:*109, 1955.

52. Baron, S.: Levels of insight and ego functioning in relation to hypnoanalysis. *Int. J. Clin. Exp. Hyp.*, *8:*141, 1960.

53. Schneck, J. M.: Hypnoanalytic observations on the psychopathology of fainting. *J. Clin. Exp. Hyp.*, *5*:167, 1957.
54. Guze, H.: Anesthesia and instrumentation trauma as revealed in hypnotherapy. *J. Clin. Exp. Hyp.*, *1*:71, 1953.
55. Barnes, R. H.: Fainting: a review of the neuropsychiatric aspects. *Amer. J. Med. Sci.*, *231*:109, 1956.
56. Kurauchi, H., and Fujita, S.: Some interesting phenomena in the hypnotic state—hypnosis and transference. *Jap. J. Psychoanal.*, *8*:1, 1961.
57. Menninger, K.: *Theory of Psychoanalytic Technique*. New York, Basic Books, 1958.
58. Schneck, J. M.: Spontaneous regression to an infant age level during self-hypnosis. *J. Genet. Psychol.*, *86*:183, 1955
59. Schneck, J. M.: Hypnotherapy in anxiety and depression, in Burton, A.: *Case Studies in Counseling and Psychotherapy*. Englewood Cliffs, N. J., Prentice-Hall, 1959.
60. Schneck, J. M.: Fragments of a hypnoanalysis. *Dis. Nerv. Syst.*, *12*:369, 1951.
61. Schneck, J. M.: The hypnoanalysis of phobic reactions. in Le Cron, L. M.: *Experimental Hypnosis*. New York, Macmillan, 1952.
62. Schneck, J. M.: Sleep paralysis. *Psychosomatics*, *2*:360, 1961.
63. Schneck, J. M.: Pseudo-malingering, *Dis. Nerv. Syst.*, *23*:396, 1962.
64. Alexander, F.: The dynamics of psychotherapy in the light of learning theory. *Amer. J. Psychiat.*, *120*:440, 1963.
65. Schneck, J. M.: Some aspects of homosexuality in relation to hypnosis. *Brit. J. Med. Hyp.*, *1*:24, Summer 1950.
66. Schneck, J. M.: Automatic writing and the hypnotic transference. *J. Gen. Psychol.*, *48*:91, 1953.
67. Kline, M. V., and Schneck, J. M.: An hypnotic experimental approach to the genesis of occupational interests and choice. *Brit. J. Med.*, *2*:2, 1950.
68. Schneck, J. M.: An hypnotic technique for the exploration of vocational interests. *J. Gen. Psychol.*, *45*:225, 1952.
69. Freud, S.: *The Interpretation of Dreams*. New York, Basic Books, 1959.
70. Schneck, J. M.: An experimental investigation of dual hypnotic dreams. *Brit. J. Med. Hyp.*, *3*:21, Summer 1952.
71. Schneck J. M.: A hypnoanalytic study of an amateur hypnotist. *Psychoanal. Rev.*, *42*:188, 1955.

NAME INDEX

A

Abt, L., 121
Ackerknecht, E. H., 46, 129, 144
Alexander, F., 18, 50, 59, 85, 196, 210
Ames, L. B., 67, 88
Arnold, M. B., 71, 86

B

Baglivi, Giorgio, 14
Bailey, Pearce, 47
Baldridge, B., 209
Barahal, H. S., 144
Barber, T. X., 71, 86
Barnes, R. H., 188, 210
Baron, S., 209
Bellak, L., 77, 78, 87
Bellamy, Edward, 7
Benedict, R., 129, 144
Bennett, L. L., 209
Bergmann, M. S., 103, 121
Berkowitz, B., 120, 176, 209
Bernheim, H., 8, 9, 10, 12, 13, 47, 70
Binet, A., 9, 47
Borelli, Giovanni, 14
Boring, E. G., 48
Bouru, 10
Bowers, M. K., 114, 120, 140, 141, 144, 176, 209
Braid, James, 9, 10, 48, 70
Bramwell, J. M., 14, 48, 92, 119
Brecher, S., 120, 140, 144, 176, 209
Brenman, M., 43, 46, 49, 66, 77, 85, 86, 88, 107, 108, 109, 121, 122, 206, 208
Breuer, Josef, 10, 11, 48
Brill, A. A., 13, 48
Brower, D., 121
Browning, Robert, 7, 47
Burot, 10
Burton, A., 17, 45, 210

C

Cardan, 5
Charcot, Jean-Martin, 8, 9, 10, 13, 47
Chertok, L., 48
Cleckley, H., 144
Conn, J. H., 125, 142, 143, 144
Cooper, L. F., 136, 144
Crasilneck, H. B., 102, 120

D

Davis, L. W., 14
de le Boë, Franz, 14
Dorcus, R. M., 208
du Maurier, George, 7, 47, 94, 119
Dunbar, H. F., 97, 120, 209

E

Ehrenwald, J., 48
Elliotson, John, 6, 10, 47
Ellis, A., 139, 144
Erickson, M. H., 36, 50, 122, 144
Esdaile, James, 6, 7, 47
Estabrooks, G. H., 92, 119
Eysenck, H. J., 209

F

Farber, L. H., 108, 121
Fenichel, O., 97, 120, 170, 188, 209
Féré, C., 9, 47
Ferenczi, S., 68, 69, 71, 77, 85
Fisher, C., 108, 121, 130, 131, 143
Fishman, S., 121
Fliess, R., 131, 144
Foveau de Courmelles, F. V., 46
Forel, A., 14, 48
Frankau, Gilbert, 47
Frazer, J. G., 4, 46, 128, 144
French, T. M., 50
Freud, S., 5, 8, 9, 10, 11, 12, 13, 14, 15,

18, 68, 69, 71, 72, 75, 77, 85, 97,
108, 120, 122, 127, 143, 169, 203,
204, 209, 210
Freytag, F. F., 146, 207
Fromm, E., 89, 119
Fujita, S., 181, 210

G
Gibson, R. W., 121
Gill, M. M., 43, 46, 66, 77, 85, 86, 88,
109, 122, 129, 130, 143, 206, 208
Gilman, T. T., 119
Goldsmith, M., 46
Goodenough, 47
Graham, H., 103, 121
Guillain, Georges, 9, 47
Guze, H., 71, 78, 86, 87, 102, 105, 120,
121, 188, 210

H
Hacker, F. J., 66, 85
Hadfield, J. A., 15, 48
Haymaker, W., 47
Hoch, P. H., 85
Horney, K., 18, 38, 45, 76, 205, 208
Hull, C. L., 15, 46, 48
Husband, R. W., 45
Huston, P. E., 122

J
James, Henry, 7, 47
Janet, P., 14, 15, 48
Jones, Ernest, 13, 48, 49, 85
Jones, J., 141, 144

K
Kanzer, M., 107, 121
Kauders, O., 48, 69, 86
Kaufman, M. R., 87
Kent, G. H., 85
Klemperer, E., 125, 126, 143, 151, 207,
208
Kline, M. V., 24, 34, 45, 46, 48, 49, 53,
55, 71, 85, 86, 87, 102, 105, 113,
120, 121, 122, 200, 210
Knight, R. P., 109, 122

Kohs, S. C., 85
Koster, S., 71, 86
Kramer, M., 209
Kris, E., 78, 87
Kubie, L. S., 49, 73, 74, 75, 87, 144
Kurauchi, H., 181, 210

L
Leavitt, H. C., 103, 121
LeCron, L. M., 49, 86, 208, 210
Lerner, M., 152, 202, 208
Liébeault, A. A., 8, 9, 10
Lincoln, A., 165
Lindner, H., 205, 206, 208
Lindner, R. M., 27, 28, 29, 43, 46, 70
86, 123, 124, 143, 145, 152, 207
London, L. S., 143
Lorand, S., 49, 204, 208
Lundholm, H., 95, 120
Luys, J., 9

M
Marcuse, F. L., 79, 87, 119
Margolin, S., 49, 74, 87
Mazer, M., 108, 121, 144
McCranie, E. J., 102, 120
McDowell, M., 122
Mead, 46
Meares, A., 35, 49, 78, 87, 123, 126, 143
Menninger, K., 130, 143, 189, 210
Mercer, M., 121
Mesmer, Franz Anton, 3, 4, 5, 6, 46, 47
Moll, A., 14, 48, 69, 85
Morton, J. H., 144
Moss, C. S., 140, 141, 144
Myers, V. R., 47

N
Nachmansohn, M., 108, 122
Nolte, J., 144

O
Oberndorf, C. P., 10, 48, 204, 208
Orne, M. T., 71, 87
O'Rourke, 105

P

Paley, A., 207
Paracelsus, 5
Pattie, F. A., 46
Poe, Edgar Allan, 7, 94, 119
Prince, Morton, 14, 15, 48

R

Rado, S., 18, 50, 73, 87, 204, 208
Raginsky, B. B., 122, 154, 208
Rapaport, D., 85
Regardie, F. I., 108, 121
Reichard, S., 49
Reiter, P. J., 92, 119
Rioch, J. M., 76, 87
Roffenstein, G., 108, 122
Rogers, C. R., 16, 48
Rosanoff, A. J., 85
Rose, R., 46, 128, 144
Rosen, George, 5
Rowland, L. W., 92, 119
Rush, B., 51, 86

S

Sarbin, T. R., 71, 86
Schilder, Paul, 15, 48, 69, 72, 75, 86
Schneck, Jerome M., viii, 4, 5, 6, 7, 8,
    9, 11, 13, 14, 15, 16, 19, 21, 23, 24,
    34, 36, 37, 38, 39, 42, 51, 52, 55,
    57, 61, 62, 63, 66, 68, 69, 70, 78,
    82, 83, 84, 85, 86, 87, 88, 89, 90,
    91, 94, 95, 96, 97, 98, 101, 103, 106,
    107, 108, 110, 112, 113, 114, 115,
    116, 118, 119, 120, 121, 127, 129,
    132, 133, 135, 137, 144, 147, 155,
    156, 160, 161, 163, 169, 170, 171,
    175, 180, 181, 187, 189, 190, 192,
    193, 194, 195, 198, 199, 200, 202,
    207, 208, 209, 210
Schrötter, K., 108, 122
Scott, N. E., 209
Seitz, P. F. D., 59, 85
Seliger, R. V., 143
Shakow, W., 122
Shor, J., 121

Sidis, B., 14, 18
Sigerist, H. E., 5, 46, 129, 144
Silverberg, W. V., 76, 87
Simmel, E., 16, 49
Solovey de Milechnin, G., 71, 88
Speyer, N., 69, 77, 85
Spiegel, H., 76, 87, 121
Spitz, R. A., 204, 208
Stillerman, B., 173, 209
Stokvis, B., 69, 77, 85
Strachey, James, 85
Sullivan, H. S., 18, 45
Sutcliffe, J. P., 141, 144
Sylvius, 14

T

Thackeray, William Makepeace, 47
Thigpen, C. H., 144
Thoma, E., 144
Thompson, C., 76, 87, 208
Thompson, M. M., 144, 203

V

Valdemar, 47
von Hartmann, 15

W

Watkins, J. G., 43, 46, 146, 154, 181,
    205, 207, 208, 209
Wechsler, I., 47
Weitzenhoffer, A., 71, 87
Wells, W. R., 91, 92, 119
White, R. W., 71, 87
White, William Alanson, 9, 48, 49
Whitman, R., 209
Williams, G. W., 39, 49
Wolberg, L. R., 43, 46, 120, 122, 146,
    207
Wolff, W., 17, 45, 120, 203, 208
Wortis, S. B., 17, 45, 85

Y

Young, P. C., 92, 119

SUBJECT INDEX

A

Alcoholism
   treatment by hypnotherapy, 145-146
Anxiety
   evaluation and treatment somatic
      symptomatology, 175-176
Anxiety and hypnoanalysis
   case report, 115
   correlation with depression, 118-119
   intial benefits hypnosis, 115
   relationship to transference issues
      present, 115
   symptom disappearance, 116
   use hypnosis for symptom relief, 115
Auto-hypnosis, 131-132
Automatic drawing, 171-173
   as attempt in understanding patient,
      172-173
   differentiation compulsive and, 171
   need for series of drawings to study,
      172
   study story told by, 172
   under hypnosis, 171, 172
   uses of, 171
Automatic writing
   use in hypnoanalysis, 24

B

Bender-Gestalt Test
   use in connection hypnosis, 24

C

Compulsive drawing, *See* Automatic
   drawing

D

Dreams
   and hypnoanalysis
      personality ingredients represented
         by, 164-165

posthypnotic suggestions to induce,
   164
remembrance details during hypnosis, of dream, 164
hypnotic, and scene visualization,
   191-193, *See also* Scene visualizations
   case reports, 191-193
   significance of, 191
Dynamic psychiatry
   defined, 3

H

Hand levitation method hypnosis
   based on ideomotor principles, 36
   two-stage technique, 36-37
   initiation of, 36
   methods of induction, 37
   patient's reaction to, 37
   use of, 32-33
Hesychast sect
   use umbilicus cord as focal point for
      trance induction, 69
House-Tree-Person test
   use in connection hypnosis, 24
   use to study influence hypnotic state,
      52-53
   comparison with Thematic Apper-
      ception test, 53
   results of tests, 52, 53
   techniques of study used, 53
   variety of subjects tested, 52-53
Hypnoanalysis
   advantages of, 3-4
   achievement symptom relief with
      hypnotherapy in framework of,
      117
      case report, 117
   aid as insight into facets of hypnosis,
      84

215

anxiety and, *See* Anxiety and hypno-
    analysis
anxiety and somatic symptomatology,
    175-176
  case report, 175-176
  evaluation and treatment of, 175
  relief of, 176
anxiety-depression correlations, 118-
    119
appearance and behavior in, 153-156
  effect passive role therapist on
    patient, 154-155
  effect claustrophobic fears on pa-
    tient, 156
  importance verbalization by pa-
    tient, 154
  influence rebirth experience con-
    cept on patient, 155-156
  phobic reactions, 156
  varying nuances of tone, timing
    and word choices, 153-154
applicability and efficacy hypnotic
    techniques, 112-113
  misleading conceptions, 112
  patient's reactions various tech-
    niques, 112-113
  techniques used, 112
  use combination of tests, 113
  use various techniques with in-
    dividual patients, 112-113
  use visual imagery and word as-
    sociation test, 113
aspects of denial, 193-194
  case illustrations, 193-194
attitudes toward treatment, 157-161
  case reports, 157-159
  need to understand goal of treat-
    ment, 160-161
  patient's fear of failure of treat-
    ment, 157
automatic drawing, *See* Automatic
    drawing
basis misunderstanding about, 3
concentrated measures and trans-
    ference implications, 177-181
  case report, 177-180
  for short term treatment, 177
  transference elements in doctor-
    patient relationship, 180-181

uses of, 180-181
concept assurance of illness reversi-
    bility, 116-117
  case reports, 116-117
  patient's need for, 116
  patient's termination treatment
    following, 116
concept dynamic hypnotic age re-
    gression, 103-106, *See also* Hyp-
    notic age regression
concept hypnotic scene visualization,
    136-137, *See also* Scene visuali-
    zation
concept trance depth and, 22-25
  classical concept of hypnotic in-
    volvement, 22
  emotional involvement patient, 25
  erroneous views of, 22
  hypnotic rating scales, 23
  posthypnotic amnesias, 22-23
  psychological content hypnotic set-
    ting, 25
  regression and revivication, 24-25,
    See also, Regression and re-
    vivication in hypnoanalysis
  somnabulistic state, 22
  use automatic writing, 24
conditions responding best to, 114
confirmation psychoanalytic obser-
    vations, 145-147
  case reports, 145-147
  in alcoholism, 145-146
  in hysteric somnabulism, case re-
    port, 145
defined, 3
definition and nature of, 3-4
denial of hypnosis, 25, 27
dependency, action and magic in,
    176-177
depth reversal during termination
    hypnotic state, 39-42
  difficulties encountered in dehyp-
    notizing, 39
  patient's reactions during termi-
    nation, 40-41
  reasons for summarized, 41-42
  reorientation period, 39
  significance, 39-40

diagnostic categories and amenability to, 113-114
conditions responding best to hypnoanalysis, 114
current trends, 114
role experience of therapist, 114
disappearance hypnotizability in successful, 129-130
doctor-patient relationship and behavior, 165-167
case report, 165
effect deceptive assessment by analyst, 165
evaluation hypnotic methods for individuals, 166
personality and hypnotic functioning of patient in, 166-167
relationship patient's behavior with expectation of therapist, 167
role of analyst in, 165
dreams and, See Dreams and hypnoanalysis
elaboration psychoanalytic observations, 126-127
exhibitionism and deception, 90-93, See also Hypnosis
fantasy, transference and countertransference, 181-186
case report using fantasy interview with therapist, 182-185
distortion of therapist by patient in, 181-182
in interviews with therapist, 181-186
use of techniques, 182
utilization of fantasy by patient, 185-186
flexibility on starting, 42-43
advantages of, 42-43
need to explore various methods gradually, 42-43
use visual imagery, 42
frequency of sessions, 20-21
case history amnesia patient, 21
dependent necessity use hypnotic interviews, 20
length individual sessions, 21
ratio hypnotic to non-hypnotic interviews, 20

growth emphasis on, 16
hidden determinants in patient's deceptive request for, 147-150
ambivalence of patient toward hypnotic techniques, 148
complications treatment due to, 148
discontinuance hypnoanalysis due patient's resistance, 148-149
need proper evaluation patient, 148-149
need to clarify ambivalence, 148
need to resolve for successful treatment, 150
negative transference, 149
patient's previous slow gains, 149-150
patient's real reluctance for use hypnotic techniques, 147-148
pressure from others on patient, 150
unconscious fantasies of patients regarding hypnosis, 147
historical antecedents and influences of, 4-16
first attempts to understand behavioral motivations, 8-9
impact Freud's work in development iatropsychology, 14
influence of Mesmer, 5-6
original iatrochemistry, 14
origins of psychoanalysis, 10
trance experiences among primitive peoples, 4-5
use in World War I, 15-16
views regarding hypnosis, See Hypnosis
hypnoanalytic explorations, 51-52
effects hypnotic setting in, 51-52
goals sought in, 51-52
significance revival buried memories, 51
hypnosis and psychological test methods, 52-56, See also Psychological test methods
hypnosis-death concept and, 93-95
hypnosis-death and hypnosis-rebirth, 127-129
case report, 127-128

similarity rites primitive tribes, 128-129
trance states and, 128-129
unconscious identifications with, 128
hypnotic contradiction of waking verbalizations and enhanced verbalization, 98-99
hypnotic control, 200
case illustration, 200
hypnotic dreams and scene visualization, See Dreams
hypnotic hallucinations and, 137-138
as external stimuli, 137
case report, 137-138
effects of various patients, 138
evaluation by patient, 137
evaluation of patients for, 137
hypnotic hallucinatory experience, 106-107
case report, 106
hypnotic imagery and second selves, 150-153
hypnotic imagery and sensory motor phenomena during, 109-112
case reports, 109, 110-111, 111-112
clues furnished psychopathology by, 110, 111-112
hypnotic paralysis, 193
case illustration, 193-194
hypnotizability, See Hypnotizability
induction phenomena, 37-39
alleged existence hypnotic state, 38
conversion reactions, 37-38
personality dynamics as basic concern, 38-39
pseudo-perfectionism, 38
psychosomatic reactions, 37
relation reactions to personality and functioning of patient, 38
initiation of, 27-30
factors in, 29-30
phases in, 27
selection of patients, 28-29
significance timing, 27, 29, 31
interpretations, psychoanalysis and, 18-19
length of treatment, 19-20
dependent on frequency of visits, 20

dependent on problems of patient, 19-20
use analysis with hypnosis, 19
limitations on symptom relief, 117-119
case report, 118
relationship between anxiety and depression, 118-119
views therapists concerning, 118
medico-legal issues involved, 92-93
role hypnotic technique and phenomena influencing, 92
case report, 92-93
misleading requests for, 30-31
motivation and goal, intellectual and emotional insight, 161-163
case reports, 161-163
multiple personalities, 140-141
nature of, 3-4
origins methods and thought in, 3
origin use of term, 15
past and present themes, 196-197
case illustration, 197
change in importance stress early events to recent, 196
patient's attitude to early experience stress, 197
perceptiveness and patient's attitude toward hypnotic experience, 99-101, See also Hypnosis
phases of, 27
phobic symptomatology, 195-196
case illustration, 195-196
premature termination of, 199
case illustration, 199
problems of symptom relief in, 56-58, See also Symptom relief
problems presented by patients entering, 55-56
productiveness and, 89-90
psychoanalysis and, See Psychoanalysis and hypnoanalysis
psychoanalysis developments incorporated in, 3
psychoanalytic explorations, 168-171
case reports, 169-171
data from integrated with treatment, 168-169

secondary rewards of therapist, 168-169
rapid investigations, 198-199
  case illustrations, 198-199
ratio somnambules to other hypnotizable subjects, 28-29
regression and revivification in, 101-102
resistance in, 43-44
  analysis of, 44
  reasons for, 44
  to authoritative role of therapist, 43
  value patient reaction to induction, 43-44
role of countertransference and transference, 35
role sexual factors in disruption induction procedure, 34
self-hypnotic dreams in, 133-136, See also Self-hypnotic dreams
significance transference-countertransference issues, 126-127
sleep paralysis, 193-194
somnambules as prospective candidates for, 28
  factors in, 29-30
spontaneous hypnotic and self-hypnotic states, 131-133
spontaneous nocturnal dreams, hypnotic dreams and, 107-109
  differentiation of, 108
  effects on patient, 108-109
  error comparison productions one patient with another, 108
  nature and implications hypnotic dreams, 107-108
  role of hypnotist in hypnotic dreams, 107
  use induced hallucinations, 107
  value hypnotic dreams to establish contact patient and therapist, 107
spontaneous remissions, 167-168
standardization of procedures, 27-28
studies early writings on, 14-15
successes and failures, 159-161
  due negative views clinicians, 160
  failure due "last chance," 159

need to understand goal of treatment for success, 160-161
superficial and deep psychotherapy, 190-191
techniques used by Raginsky, 154
transference in, 44-45
  fallacy need for positive, 44-45
  necessity analysis transference reactions, 45
  role analyst, 45
treatment of an entrenched phobia, 146-147
two-stage hand levitation technique, See Hand levitation technique
use hypnography, 123
use hypnotic interviews, 20-21
use of, 31
use of term, 15-16, 206
use to evaluate and treat somatic manifestations, 175
use to explore role illness as neurotic defense, 152
value of, 16-19
  as field of scientific medical concern, 16-17
  claims regarding therapeutic efficacy, 17
  effectiveness hypnotic methods, 19
  factors in benefits of, 17-18
variations in spontaneous verbalizations, 163
  case report, 163
views structure of, 123-126
  change of body image, 125-126
  desirability frequency of hypnosis in treatment, 126
  evaluation motivation request for hypnosis, 126
  induction posthypnotic amnesia following hypnotic recall, 123-124
  influence patient by emotional tone hypnotic setting, 125
  limited aspects of one or two sessions, 123
  patient-centered psychotherapy, 125
  techniques used by Lindner, 123-125

use hypnography by Meares, 123
variations and flexibility in therapeutic approach, 125
visual imagery and hallucinations in,
95-98
Hypnography
as method in hypnoanalysis, 123
Hypnosis
aid in verbalization, 99
case report, 99
alleged simulation of, 194
and psychological test methods, 52-
56, See also Psychological test
methods
animal, 79
approach of Charcot to, 8, 9
approach of Freud to, 8
as an artifact, 141-142
as catalytic agent, 173
assessment of, 6
applied to hypnoanalysis, 6
basic difference ideas Charcot and
Freud regarding, 8
behavior, expectation and artifact,
141-142
case report, 142
patient's behavior influenced by
therapist's expectations, 142
shades and degrees of behavioral
changes, 142
validity of regression, 141-142
closed versus open eyes, 23-24
common misconceptions, 203
concept defensive productivity in relation to, 138-140
case reports, 139
failures encountered, 140
reactions of patients, 138-139
contradicting statements made during hypnotic and non-hypnotic
states, 98-99
case reports, 98-99
contributions of Braid, 9-10
denial of, 25-27, 194
basis for, 25
case illustrating, 25-27
handling of, 25-26
dependency, action, and magic in,
176-177

difficulties hypnotizability of patients,
10-11
difficulty in, due rejection, 12
dynamics of interest in, 200-202
case illustration patient-hypnotist,
201-202
identification of hypnosis with
power by patient, 201
needs of therapist in hypnotic relationships, 200-201
patient as amateur hypnotist, 201
patient as healer, 202
entertainment, 90-91
effects of, 90-91
interest of patient in, 91
interest to hypnoanalyst, 90-91
equation state of with death, 93-94
exhibitionism and deception, 90-93
influence entertainment hypnosis
on patient, 90-91
medico-legal issues involved, 92-93
use of by hypnoanalyst, 90
utilization of for anti-social purposes, 91-92
focus attention during induction, 32
ability to note variations in sensation and emotions, 32-33
achievement eye closure, 32
awareness of feeling tone, 32, 33
increasing awareness of psychological response, 32, 33
participation in hand levitation,
32-33
role transference and countertransference, 35
homosexuality equations and, 197-
198
case illustrations, 197-198
misunderstanding regarding, 31-32
basis of, 3
of patients, 31-32
multiple personalities in, 140
nature and theories of, 69-81
basic fallacies of theories, 79
basic state of hypnosis, 80
correlation with changes in personality and psychoanalytic
theories, 77-78

essence of hypnotic experiences, 79-80
  Hesychast sect, 69
  hypnotic as extension processes
    normal attention, 74
  interpersonal elements and trans-
    ference features, 72-73
  libidinal elements, 72
  phylogenetic theory, 78-81
  regression, 80-81
  relationship between hypnoanalyst
    and patient, 70
  role suggestion in, 70
  role transference in, 71
  summary, 75-77
  theoretical significance sexual ele-
    ments in transference, 69-70
  trance behavior and expression, 69
  transference elements in, 69, 70
  varied aspects hypnotic process and
    state, 73-74
  various "states" involved in, 75
  various theories encompassed in, 81
  view toward therapist of Freud, 71-
    72
obsessive-compulsive personality type
    patient, 99-100
  case report, 100
phases of, 74
phylogenetic concept of, 78-81
posthypnotic amnesias, 22-24
pseudo-malingering, 194-195
reactions to, 32-33
  psychosomatic reactions to induc-
    tion, 33-34
  resistance behavior, 34
  sexual factors and, 34-35
reactions to as reflections of person-
    ality attributes, 173-175
  case report, 173-175
  emergence early in treatment, 173
  establishment relationship to ther-
    apist by, 173
  interpretation of to patient, 174-
    175
re-evaluations of, 6
historical importance of, 6
relinquishment work with by Freud,
    10-13

role non-verbal cues in non-hypnotic
    therapy and, 35-36
role sexual factors in disruption in-
    duction procedure, 34-35
secondary personalities in, 140-141
self-hypnosis, 131-133
  case report, 132
  considerations in use of, 132-133
  evaluation patients experiencing,
    131-132
  use of, 133
spontaneous
  as manifestation of resistance, 131
  potential usefulness, 131
spontaneous regression under, 186-
    190
  advantages, 187
  case report, 187, 188-189
  focus misleading when on regres-
    sion only, 187
  following build-up by earlier per-
    sonality evaluations, 187
  practical use of, 189
  preparation for, 187
  reactions patients to, 189-190
spontaneous sensory and motor phe-
    nomena, 63-69
  alterations in state of ego, 66
  as reflection transference issues, 68
  cases illustrating, 63-66
  extent and complexity of, 66
  phenomena related to bilaterality,
    66-67
  therapeutic significance of, 63
suggestibility, 60-61
tests used in connection with, 24
theories regarding Freud's rejection
    of, 13
transference reaction, 11-12
transference and transference anal-
    ysis, 129-131
  posthypnotic suggestions to induce
    dreams, 130-131
  views of stress on transference in-
    volvements, 129-130
two-stage hand levitation method,
    36-37
unconscious identification with homo-
    sexuality, 68-69

use by ancient man, 5
use defensive reactions to, 36
use for relief anxiety, 114-116
use sodium penetothal intravenously
    to deepen, 130
use theme of in literature, 7-8
views of Horney, 205
views of Liébault and Bernheim re-
    garding, 8-9
views of Lorand, 204-205
views of Oberndorf, 204
views of Rado, 204
views of Spitz, 204
Hypnosis-death concept, 93-95
as conscious association with resem-
    blance implication, 93, 95
as defense reaction by patient, 94
case report, 94-95
hypnosis-rebirth following, 127-129
need of patient to reject feeling of,
    93-94
relationship to other psychodynamic
    issues, 94
Hypnotherapy
achievement symptom relief with
    within framework of hypnoanal-
    ysis, 117
case report, 117
dependency, action and magic in,
    176-177
use of term, 206
Hypnotherapy, psychoanalytic, See Psy-
    choanalytic hypnotherapy
Hypnotic age regression
dynamic versus chronological, 104-
    105
effects in revivification, 104-105
results Rorschach tests given one
    patient, 103
results when patient allowed latitude,
    104
studies in hypnotic progression, 105-
    106
total regression versus regression to
    indefinite past, 104
utilization of in practice of hypno-
    analysis, 103-104
Hypnotic imagery and second selves,
    150-153

case illustrations of a second self, 152-
    153
case reports, 152-153
introduction variations hypnotic tech-
    niques, 150-151
Klemperer's presenting of watcher
    phenomenon, 151-152
significance illness as neurotic de-
    fense, 152
Hypnotizability
predictability of, 33
    by clinical assessments of patients
        by hypnoanalysts, 33
    purpose of, 33
    studies made, 33
    use Rorschach test, 33

I
Iatropsychology
impact Freud's work in development
    of, 14
influence of psychosomatics, 14
relation to psychiatry, 14
role of psychobiology in, 14
Impulsive drawing, See Automatic
    drawing

M
Mesmerism
application Mesmer's methods today,
    5-6
contribution Elliotson, 6
mid-nineteenth century proponents
    of, 6-7
theories of Esdaile, 7
Minnesota Multiphasic Personality In-
    ventory, 24
Multiple personality theme, 140-141
association with fugue states and
    amnesias, 141
in history of hypnosis and psycho-
    pathology, 140
secondary personalities, 140-141
theories concerning, 141

N
Nancy School of hypnosis, 8

O

Omphalopsychics, *See* Hesychast sect

P

Paris School of Hypnosis, 8
Phylogenetic theory of hypnosis, 78-81
Posthypnotic amnesia
concept and use of, 22-24
Psychoanalysis
and hypnoanalysis, 18-19, 202-207
advantages combining, 205-207
comparisons by Lerner, 202
factors in impossibility comparisons
of, 203-204
resistance patients to hypnoanalysis, 202
transference ties in, 205
treatment of choice for various
problems, 202
various opinions regarding, 204-205
dependency, action and magic in,
176-177
length of treatment, 19
origins of, 10
role of Janet in origin of, 15
Psychoanalytic hypnotherapy, 81-84
abreaction, 81-83
basic role of, 82
evaluation, 81-82
fantasies of patients, 83
fugue state, 84
case report, 84
insight into and related concerns,
83-84
need for understanding patient and
therapist, 83-84
significance of, 82
wartime settings involved, case report, 82-83
Psychological test methods, 52-56
as supplement to clinical findings in
hypnoanalysis, 52
importance hypnosis in, 52-56
use House-Tree-Person test, 52, 53
use Thematic Apperception test, 53-54
use word association procedure, 55

Psychotherapy
psychoanalytic contribution Freud
to, 3
scientific beginnings of, 3
Productiveness and hypoanalysis, 89-90
erroneous view regarding potential
for, 89
potential for, 89
qualities in patient necessary for potential for, 89-90
source erroneous view regarding potential for, 89

R

Regression and revivification in hypnoanalysis, 101-102
case report, 101-102
due emotional insight preceding intellectual insight, 102
range of experience in, 102
Rorschach test
use in connection hypnosis, 24
use in prediction hypnotizability, 33

S

Scene visualization, 136-137
differentation from hypnotic dream,
136
differentation hallucinatory occurrence, 136-137
nature of, 136
use of term, 136
School of the Hospital de la Charité
combining Schools of Paris and
Nancy, 9
Self-hypnotic dreams, 133-136
case reports, 134-136
nightmare quality of, 135-136
similarity to dual, 133
study of form and content of, 133
use of in hypnoanalysis, 135
use of to intensify hypnoanalytic
activity, 133-134
Somnambulism
expression hysteria in form of, 145
case report, 145

Suggestibility and hypnosis, 60-61
    effect on hypnotizability of patients,
        61
    reaction patient to awareness, 61
Symptom alleviation, *See* Symptom re-
    lief
Symptom relief, 56-63
    alleviation symptoms without special
        attention, 59
    application principles psychotherapy
        within hypnoanalytic setting, 62-
        63
    approach various hypnoanalysts, 56-
        57
    by personality growth, 58
    dependence on nature transference
        relationship, 58-59
    evaluation factors involved, 61-62
    evaluation transference in, 62
    implications role of therapist as au-
        thority, 59
    operation of transference in, 62
    patient's need for authority and au-
        thority substitution, 59
    case reports, 59-60
    problems in, 56-60
        attempt alleviation prior to hyp-
            nosis, 57
        recurrence of symptoms, 57-58
        substitution new symptoms after
            relief, 57-58

T

Thematic Apperception Test
    use in connection with hypnosis, 24
    use to study influence hypnotic state,
        53-55
        case reports, 53-55
        effects hypnotic state on, 53
        methods administration, 53
        use with House-Tree-Person test,
            53
Trance, *See also* Hypnosis
    role of, 4-5
    use among primitive peoples, 4-5

V

Visual imagery and hallucinations in
    hypnoanalysis, 95-98
    case reports, 95-96, 96-97, 97-98
    differentiation closed and open eye
        imagery, 96
    frequency auditory, 95
    frequency visual, 95
    importance of, 97
    necessity to understand significance
        of, 95

W

Watcher phenomenon, 151
Wechsler-Bellevue scale
    use in connection hypnosis, 24